CAGE AND AVIARY SERIES

PHEASANTS AND THEIR ENEMIES

OTHER CAGE AND AVIARY BOOKS

The Pheasants of the World
Dr. Jean Delacour

Rare Pheasants of the World
D. Grenville Roles

The Gloster Fancy Canary
John S. Cross

Ornamental Waterfowl
A.A. Johnson and W.H. Payn

PHEASANTS
AND
THEIR ENEMIES

The Story of Pheasants

By

JAMES O'C FITZSIMONS

Illustrated by
Jennifer Kingston

SECOND EDITION

Published by: SPUR PUBLICATIONS
SAIGA PUBLISHING CO LTD
1 Royal Parade
Hindhead, Surrey GU26 6TD, England

First published 1963
Second edition 1979

© Saiga Publishing Co. Ltd. 1979

ISBN 0 904558 56 8

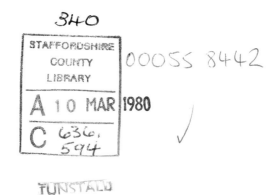
Typeset by Inforum Ltd., Portsmouth
Printed in Great Britain
in 11-point Baskerville type
by The Pitman Press, Bath

FOREWORD

I have known Dr Fitzsimons personally for some time, but long before this I knew of his interest in keeping birds, particularly exotic pheasants, which he kept at his home in Naas and with which he had many successes in breeding.

Throughout Ireland he has become well known to aviculturists and his advice had been sought by many and had always been readily given. This little book which has been written from his personal experiences should prove a great help to all who decide to keep pheasants as a hobby. His chapter on diseases, while brief, covers the main problems which one is likely to find in a pheasantry. The notes on feeding and rearing cannot fail to be of value, while his detailed description of the species makes identification simple.

The whole work makes instructive reading both for the beginner and the expert alike, and it should provide a textbook that no one who is interested in pheasants should be without.

I wish Dr Fitzsimons every success with this comprehensive and delightful book.

TERRY MURPHY
Superintendent, the Dublin Zoo

PREFACE

There is no more delightful hobby for the tired worker, or indeed for anybody else, than the breeding and care of birds. Pheasants are the most fascinating of all, and provide much real pleasure in the study of the habits and display of each individual from the day they leave the egg. The care and upbringing of pheasants presents no special mystery or difficulty and it takes only a short time every day to supply their wants. The simple rules one must observe are strict cleanliness, protection from infection, proper feeding and shelter: these are the essentials. Pheasants are as easy to keep as domestic poultry and cost less to feed.

In this book I tried to set down some of my own experiences of over thirty years. Such success as I have achieved over this period came only after a long period of trial and error, many heartaches and disappointments. As a lover of birds it gave me great pleasure to write it and I trust the reader will enjoy reading it every bit as much.

J. O'C. F.

PUBLISHER'S FOREWORD

In publishing this new edition we hope it will provide an *introductory* text to supplement our existing titles. The main drawings are by Jennifer Kingston, but additional vignettes have been included to show the detailed feather formation of these beautiful birds. These are from old drawings by A.F. Lydon.

CONTENTS

Page

Blackneck: Chinese Ringneck; Mongolian; Versicolor; Reeves; Golden; Swinhoe; Copper; Argus; Cheer; Elliot; Mikado; Melanistic Mutant; White.

Crossoptilon; Tragopan; Kalijs; Lady Amherst; Peacock Pheasant; Firebacks; White Tailed Wattled; Blood; Monols; Imperial; Kolass; Edward's; Prince of Wales.

Peafowl; Jungle Fowl; Hybrids; Megapodes.

Feeding chicks; Feeding adults; Feeding in the wild; Laying down stock; Releasing.

COLOURED ILLUSTRATIONS

ix

LIST OF MONOCHROME ILLUSTRATIONS

CHAPTER I

INTRODUCTION

Pheasant keepers the world over are indebted to that great ornithologist, M. Jean Delacour, who is without doubt the greatest living authority on the subject, and is to pheasants what Peter Scott is to wildfowl. When fifteen years old, M. Delacour had the largest collection of birds in the world. He travelled throughout Asia, through tropical forests, jungles, swamps and mountain ranges, in places where no white man had ever ventured before. He collected many hitherto unknown varieties and succeeded in taking most of them back to Europe alive. Before this, many of the rarer pheasants were known only from specimens of their skins preserved in museums.

Among varieties taken home alive by M. Delacour were Edward's, Bels, Germain's Peacock pheasant, the lovely Crested Argus and the very rare Imperial pheasant. Afterwards he bred them all in France and laid the foundation of all stocks of their kind in captivity. M. Delacour's collection was totally destroyed in France during the First World War. When it was over he built up another. This second one was the finest in the world but it also was destroyed during the Second World War. Not to be beaten, he went to live in California, where he has yet again built up a fine collection. In America some fifty varieties are now freely bred.

Previous to the efforts of M. Delacour, birds usually died on the voyage to Europe. They were caught by natives perhaps several months before and carried in baskets for hundreds of miles through forest and jungle before reaching the bird markets. They were then put on board ship and set out on the long journey to Europe, without proper food, exposed to tropical sun, overcrowded and completely uncared for. In their natural state many varieties are becoming extinct. Natives trap them by erecting hundreds of yards of low brushwood fences in the pheasant haunts, with openings every few yards over which nooses are set. If not inspected frequently the birds will choke or damage themselves by struggling, or else they are taken by predators.

The captured birds are sent for export or killed for their plumes. Were it not for the concern of aviculturists and for specimens bred in aviaries and game farms they would be lost for ever. The beautiful Mikado and Swinhoe are said to be extinct in Formosa, their country of origin.

Almost thirty years ago I saw my first Golden pheasant in the aviary of a friend and there and then I determined to own a pair. I already had several large aviaries containing different varieties of foreign birds, canaries and finches. I learned that pheasants would not harm them so I purchased a pair of Goldens to be followed by pairs of Lady Amherst, Reeves, Elliots and Silvers. These were obtained from Mr P. J. Lambert of Yorkshire, then Secretary of the Ornamental Pheasant Society, which was founded in 1935. The Society's Journal ceased publication in 1939, on the outbreak of war; by that time there were 600 members. I later obtained some of the rarer varieties from the late Dr Hastings Weir of Lifford, Co. Donegal. As well as having a wonderful collection of pheasants, Dr Weir had also probably the finest collection of ducks in Europe at that time. He had twenty-eight different species of ducks.

Since all pheasants are extremely beautiful, comparisons are out of the question. Each species has its own characteristics: arrogant, playful, contemptuous, bored. The different reactions to fear, joy, love and sociability are apparent almost from the day they are hatched.

Most varieties of pheasants are polygamous. Polygamy is found in species of birds where the male is brilliantly coloured and the female plain. In polygamous species the male does nothing but eat, mate and preserve his own life. Monogamous species of pheasants take on their share of nest making, incubating and rearing young.

All birds and animals are very sensitive to sound waves but this applies in marked degree to pheasants. Their hearing mechanism is so acute that they can appreciate earth tremors caused by human footsteps at a distance. The Japanese, great pheasant lovers, who suffer continuously from earthquakes, have noticed signs of distress or uneasiness in the birds when one is imminent. They become unsettled, dash about wildly and call in alarm. Seismographic recordings show that the finest of earth tremors, not noticed by humans, are evidenced by the behaviour of birds, dogs, cats, horses and cattle. This can happen many hours or days before a major earthquake and gives, in a great many instances, due warning.

With the exception of Silver and Crossoptilon, it is not recommended that ornamental pheasants be kept at liberty otherwise than on a large isolated wooded estate with no other trees within miles. They are inclined to wander and become prey to predatory birds and animals.

It is not cruel, as some people imagine, to confine pheasants in aviaries. They are ground birds essentially and will always run in preference to flying. Although there is a vast difference in the lives of pheasants in the wild and in captivity, it is extraordinary how quickly they adapt themselves to the latter. They are happy and contented, although they must eat food without the variety they are used to and get no flying or running exercise.

Many varieties of pheasants will settle down immediately and become tame in captivity, although in their native habitat they are among the wildest of creatures. On the other hand, when we consider our native, almost domesticated species, they will never settle down in aviaries or captivity. The common woodquest, even though hand-reared, can never be tamed. The wildgoose, one of the wildest and shyest, becomes fearless and will eat from the hand a few days after being caught up.

Pheasants which are reared and cared for in aviaries, once having escaped, will make every effort to get back in again. Some of my valuable birds have escaped, risen and flown off. Invariably they returned in a day or so and when caught up and returned to their quarters they were delighted, as was shown by their chuckling to their comrades. They immediately set about feeding and preening themselves. This applies to almost all foreign birds when confined in aviaries. Several of my Australian and African finches and waxbills are now at liberty. They originally escaped through an unknown small opening in the wire netting. They remained around the garden all day but always went back to their sleeping quarters in the evening. They are now allowed full freedom.

Figure 1 GOLD AND SILVER PHEASANTS
(*Thaumalea picta and Euplocamus nycthemerus*).

Chapter 2

HISTORY

Some hundreds of millions of years ago, during the long Carboniferous epoch, the first air-breathing creatures came out from the waters: they were called Amphibia, from the Greek words meaning double life. They lived near water and their young, as larvae quite unlike their parents in appearance, grew to adult form in the water. Later, in the Permian period, the reptiles appeared, crawling, as their name, derived from the Latin, implies; and still later the birds evolved.

It may seem a far cry from creeping reptile to flying bird, but they resemble one another in that the offspring of both develop in eggs and emerge in a form resembling their parents. Our childhood conception of birds is associated with flying, feathers and eggs; feathers also come into the picture of their evolution with the earliest bird fossil known, Archaeopteryx. This bird-like creature is regarded as the link between reptile and bird because it still had a long reptilian tail and teeth but reptilian scales had been transformed into well-developed feathers. It is easy to imagine how small tree-climbing reptiles began to jump from branch to branch and how Archaeopteryx or one of its near relatives spread its feathers and flew: the progenitor of the birds.

The Jurassic stratum in which this fossil was found occurs long ages after the time of reptilian precursor fossils. The stretches of time taken for these evolutionary changes can only be approximately judged in years, but they certainly lasted for millions of generations. Due to different climates, food and environment, divergent characteristics were evolved which led to the gradual formation of the various tribes of birds, among them the pheasants. Meanwhile, Archaeopteryx disappeared from the earth.

Pheasants, all retaining the same common habits and anatomical structure, though living in different environmental conditions, finally remained scattered all over Asia, with one species in Africa. None are indigenous to Europe.

The first pheasant to be introduced into Europe was *Phasianus colchicus*—the Blacknecked pheasant. It was supposed to have been brought by the Argonauts from Asia Minor some 1200 years before the Christian era; Jason possibly had a hand in it when he was sent to fetch the Golden Fleece from Colchis. The pheasants came from the banks of the River Phacis, now the River Rioni, where it flows from the Caucasus into the Black Sea at Colchis—hence the name, Phasianus in Latin, Pheasant in English, Faisan in French, Fagiano in Italian and Fasan in German. Wars have changed the place names, but the pheasant remains the same.

The Blackneck held sway until the introduction of *Phasianus torquatus*, the Chinese Ringnecked pheasant which has a white ring almost surrounding the neck. Some authorities think that the Romans obtained this species from the Greeks and took it to England along with the fallow deer and the rabbit. Afterwards, the Versicolor or Green pheasant of Japan and the Mongolian pheasant from Turkestan were introduced, in 1840 and 1898 respectively. They all hybridised freely and it is now accepted that they are the ancestors of our present game bird. *Phasianus torquatus* is the dominant species, which explains why so many wild pheasants have a white neck-ring.

The date of introduction into England is not exactly known, though pheasants were mentioned in King Harold's time as a royal bird. King Henry VIII was one of the first to raise and fatten the birds for the table and a French priest was employed to supervise their rearing. The birds were served wearing head, neck, back and tail feathers, a custom which came from Constantinople. The pheasant ousted the peacock from this special honour and pheasant was a dish reserved for kings and emperors. They were protected as royal game and penalties for illegal taking were very severe.

During the reign of Louis XV of France the pheasant was abundant in royal parks. They became extinct after the revolution in France. When peace came the pheasant population was restored and they now flourish almost all over the world.

The pheasant is a gallinaceous bird, a scratcher and beak

digger of the same family as domestic poultry, guinea fowl, turkey, peafowl, partridge, quail and black grouse. It belongs to a family of birds whose young can feed themselves and run from the time they leave the shell. They are usually large birds of lovely colour and deportment. The head is often denuded of feathers. In most varieties males have large spurs and strong legs for running and scratching. Their wings are short and round, hence they can fly for short distances only, at a speed of about thirty miles per hour. They are exhausted after more than about one and a half miles.

Figure 2   VERSICOLOR, or JAPANESE PHEASANTS
(*Phasianus versicolor*).

CHAPTER 3

VARIETIES OF PHEASANT: ONE

A species has distinctive common characteristics. A variety is a subdivision of a species. A variety cannot be distinguished from a species. Why one species is rare and confined to a small area and another is common and widespread is difficult to explain. Between species and sub-species about two hundred varieties of pheasant are known to exist.

Groups

Observers have divided pheasants into different groups from their habits, colour, shape, ears, ruffs, crests, spurs, number and colour of eggs, moulting, nesting, mating habits and display. Beebe, that great American ornithologist, classified pheasants into four groups from the way they moult their tail feathers. Other observers have divided them into sixteen groups from all their different characteristics. Each group differs in many respects from other groups, but the relationship between the members of each group is obvious. All groups resemble each other in the pattern of size, colour and number of eggs laid. Some are very closely related, such as the Golden and Amherst. They differ only in colour, they cross freely and the progeny is fertile. The same applies to their near relations, the true or game pheasants. Members of different groups may hybridise but the progeny is not fertile.

When discussing varieties, the Blackneck, Ringneck, Mongolian, Versicolor, Melanistic Mutant and the rare Bohemian are referred to as Game pheasants: a misnomer, but an easy classification in order to distinguish them from others, which in Europe are only suitable as aviary specimens. In the wild, a purebred is now impossible to find since they all hybridised; however, some specimens are still in existence in aviaries and game farms. They were freely imported before the Second

World War. They are the true pheasants and their natural habitat is over most of Asia.

BLACKNECK (*Phasianus colchicus*)

The natural habitat of the Blackneck is in the Caucasus and along the Black Sea. Blacknecks cover most of Asia in temperatures ranging from tropical heat to high mountain coldness. Like all true pheasants they have ears, pointed tails, round wings and no ruffs. They are birds of open spaces and unlike other pheasants, they avoid deep forests. There are several sub-species.

In the male, the head and neck are purplish green, somewhat darker than that of the other true pheasants. There is no white neck-ring. The face and wattles are crimson; the breast and flanks are reddish bronze; the colour is difficult to describe accurately since all the different shades blend into each other, giving a beautiful overall metallic sheen. The wings are grey; the tail is greenish with light brown bars.

The females are a dull greyish brown and like almost all female pheasants, they conform and align themselves to their natural surroundings for survival in the nesting season. Nature here cares nothing for appearances except as a means of survival.

The eggs are olive brown and take twenty-three days to hatch. In the wild, ten to twelve eggs are laid. If the eggs are destroyed the hen will lay a second clutch and perhaps a third. In captivity, up to fifty eggs may be laid. The young are fertile when ten months old and they are in full plumage at six months old.

CHINESE RINGNECK (*Phasianus colchicus torquatus*)

The natural home of this bird is China.

Another true pheasant, its colouring is much the same as that of others of the species. The head and neck are purplish and the bird may be distinguished by a white ring around the neck, interrupted at the front. The mantle is golden; the breast and sides are reddish blue; the flanks are yellowish with blue markings; the tail is long, pointed, brown and barred. The female is the same colour as the female Blackneck.

The eggs are olive or green and take twenty-three days to

hatch. Up to fifty eggs may be laid if the female is not allowed to incubate. The young are fertile at one year old. They attain adult plumage at six months old.

MONGOLIAN (*Phasianus colchicus mongolius*)

This is another member of the family of true pheasants. It is a native of Turkestan and not of Mongolia. It is the most beautiful of its species and a purebred male has no equal in bird life for stateliness and dignity. The head and neck are purplish violet blue. The head is topped with a white cap, and a deep white ring, interrupted at the front, surrounds the neck. The back is silvery brown and the rump is metallic green. The wings are silvery grey; the breast is maroon with a metallic sheen; the face and wattles are crimson; the bill is ivory; the tail is long, pointed, brown and barred.

The female is brownish grey with brown spots.

The olive brown eggs take twenty-three days to hatch. Up to thirty eggs may be laid. The young are in full plumage and fertile at one year old.

VERSICOLOR or GREEN PHEASANT (*Phasianus versicolor*)

This bird is a native of Japan and adjacent islands. It is a true pheasant and is closely related to the Ringneck and Blackneck. In the male the head and breast are purplish green; the throat is blue; the back is chestnut and the underparts are green; the wings are blue; the rump is green; the wing coverts are grey, streaked with blue. The bird has no neck-ring.

The female is a darker grey than the other members of the family and it is the smallest of the true pheasants.

A friendly bird, in its wild state in Japan it stays close to towns and villages. It is a very fast flyer. The eggs, twelve in number, are olive green, taking twenty-four days to hatch. Like all true pheasants, it attains full plumage and is fertile in the first year.

REEVES (*Syrmaticus reevesi*)

The Reeves, or Bartailed pheasant, a native of Central China, lives up to 6000 ft in mountain ranges. It is the largest of all pheasants. These birds are powerfully fast flyers, reaching 40 miles per hour, and are noted for the fact that when in flight they can stop in their own length by setting their wings as a brake. They are very easy to rear and keep in aviaries. They are supposed to be bad-tempered, but I never found this to be so except in the breeding season.

In the male, the head is white surrounded by a black cowl. The neck has a large white ring. The back, breast and general body colour is golden yellow with black and maroon bars; the underparts are maroon. The tail, 5 ft in length, is buff with dark bars. There are no ears, tufts or crests.

Figure 3. *Golden Pheasant*

The female is a dull light brown, streaked with maroon and white.

In their natural habitat Reeves pheasants are nearly extinct, because the long tail feathers are much sought after by the natives for ceremonial headwear. The eggs, buff in colour, take twenty-six days to hatch—usually up to twenty may be laid. One of my Reeves hens laid an egg every second day from the 10th April to the 7th August. The birds reach full maturity, plumage and fertility in their first year.

GOLDEN (*Chryslophus pictus*)

This is a ruffed pheasant, a native of Eastern and Central China. There is only one species and no sub-species. Of all birds on earth, the Golden pheasant is, in my opinion, easily the most beautiful. The gorgeous plumage is illustrated in lacquer work, tapestries, silks, and various works of Chinese art over the ages.

Its nest has never been found and little is known of its habits in the wild. It was first imported into Europe over 200 years ago. There is a painting in the Wallace Collection of a Golden pheasant, signed by J. B. Fanvelet, 1819–90.

The Golden is purely an aviary bird and does not take well to freedom; although it has been set at liberty on large estates it has never flourished there. It is very hardy, breeds freely, and is delightfully tame.

The male is continually on the move, displaying his gorgeous plumage to the full in a manner difficult to describe. He spreads his neck cape like a fan and dances around the females. At intervals he suddenly stands perfectly still in the middle of the dance with flashing eyes, peeping from under the fan and uttering a hissing sound like a snake. This performance goes on for hours and is marvellous to watch. The females take little notice; when they become bored they just fly on to a high perch.

The male is clothed in scarlet, crimson, blue and gold. The underparts and breast are crimson, without a trace of yellow. The wings are brown and black; the secondary wing feathers are purple; the tail is long and pointed and is brown and spotted without any dark bars; the cape and neck feathers are orange; the mantle is metallic green and the legs are yellow. No artist could produce such a wonderful blending of colours, iridescent, radiant, majestic.

The female is a dull brown colour with yellow legs and beak. She will lay up to forty cream coloured eggs in a season. The young are easily reared and the incubation period is twenty-three days. The female never leaves the nest for food or drink when hatching.

Golden males will not put on full plumage until they are one year old and they are not fertile until they are two years old. They are very hardy and they are not affected by the severest weather. Many thousands are trapped in China to supply anglers' tackle and ladies' hat plumes. Unfortunately, the females, which are worthless for this trade, are also destroyed and the species is in danger of extermination.

A mutation of the Golden has occurred in captivity—the Blackthroated Golden—which breeds true. Most Golden pheasants of today show some contamination caused by crossing with the Amherst. Yellow marking on the chest, tail barring, green on the upper back and pale yellow legs all tend to indicate impurity.

SWINHOE (*Gennaeus swinhoii*)

A native of the high mountains of Formosa. In the male, the head is black, the face crimson; the crest and mantle are white; two of the tail feathers are white, the others are brown; the underparts are purple; the wing coverts are crimson and green; the legs are crimson and the bill is yellow.

The female is rusty coloured with black markings. The eggs take twenty-six days to hatch.

This is one of the most noble and beautiful pheasants in existence. It is now commonly found in aviaries in Europe and America. I found my specimens very tame and trusting, although one great drawback when breeding is that the male is liable to savage his mate if she has no place to hide when he attacks.

The first pair to arrive in Europe, almost 100 years ago, were bought by a member of the Rothschild family for £250. They are now comparatively cheap, costing about £30 per pair.

The male shows himself to the best advantage in the mating season. He dances around the female with head crest and scarlet wattles standing erect, wings spread and body plumage scintillating into a mystical entanglement of colours. He never seems to tire of performing.

COPPER PHEASANT (*Syrmaticus soemmeringi*)

This is another member of the true pheasant group of the Genus Syrmaticus which includes the long tails in Reeves, Elliot and Mikado. The only difference, apart from colour, is that the Copper pheasant has eighteen, instead of sixteen, tail feathers as in the others. The birds are indigenous to Japan, where they are known as Yamadori "Pheasants of the Mountains".

In the male, the colouring is generally of a reddish copper hue. The head and neck are red; the wings are brown, black and white; there is an unusual white crescent-shaped patch under each eye. They are hardy and easy to breed if you are lucky enough to get a male that will not murder his mate. They are very plentiful in their own country but rare in

America and Europe where they were introduced almost 100 years ago; although liberated in England several years ago they never bred.

The female is a dull coppery brown colour. There are five sub-species all differing in colour. Although it lives with the Versicolor, or Green pheasant, the Copper has never hybridised. On an average ten cream coloured eggs are laid. The incubation period is twenty-four days. Beyond a whirring of wings they do not display.

ARGUS (*Phasianus argus*)

There are two main species—the Great Argus and the Crested Argus. This bird is really one of nature's wonders; related to the peacock, it is the Phoenix of Classical mythology. The highest gift to the Chinese Emperors was an Argus pheasant.

The display of the male is one of the most amazing things in bird life. In the mating season he selects a piece of territory and makes a clearing about 18 ft square. From this everything is removed—sticks, grass or any obstruction. This is his playground where he performs his dances and display. He calls to the females and when they gather around, he proceeds to show himself off. His wings are thrust upwards like those of a swan. His head is bent backwards as if pretending to hide it among the wing feathers, through which he occasionally peeps to see if his lady friends are taking any notice. This performance is kept up until one or more females signify their intention of staying on by making low chuckling sounds. When courtship is over, nesting begins. Two buff coloured eggs, splashed with reddish brown spots, are laid. Incubation takes twenty-five days, during which the female never leaves the nest for food or drink. All species do not reach full plumage until they are three years old.

The Great Argus (Argusianus argus argus) inhabits the jungles all over Malaya, Borneo and Sumatra. Except in the mating season it lives a solitary life.

In different localities variations in colouring occur. The top of the head is covered with black short feathers, with a black velvety crest in the centre. The neck is bare and the neck skin blue; the wings are huge and brown, spotted buff and white; tail covert yellow, spotted black; the back is yellow; the breast and underparts are reddish, streaked with buff and black; the legs are red without spurs and the beak is ivory. The tail is long chestnut and covered with white spots and large yellow centred ocelli with a black surrounding circle.

The female is brown with black and buff markings. Two eggs are laid and take twenty-four days to hatch.

These birds are uncommon in Europe and America, where they have been bred but not freely. They were first imported eighty years ago.

Rheinarts Crested Argus (*Rheinartia ocellata*) is a native of the dense forests of Annam from sea level to 5000 ft. Its habits are similar to those of the Great Argus. A sub-species has occurred but it has never been imported alive.

The plumage in the male is ocellated with eye-like spots and gives an illusion of the ill-fated Argus of mythology, the hundred-eyed shepherd, who was sent by Juno to watch Io and whose hundred eyes never closed in sleep until charmed by the lyre of Mercury.

The head of this magnificent bird is clothed in black short velvety feathers. The back of the neck is grey and black; the rest of the neck is naked blue skin. The wings, of normal size, are brown with buff spots; the back is yellow with black spots; the legs are red; the beak is pink. The tail is over 5 ft long and is carried in a cascade. It is beautifully coloured brown with red spots and ocellated.

The female is dull brown marked with black spots.

The two eggs are buff coloured and take twenty-three days to hatch.

Malay Crested Argus (*Rheinartia ocellata ingresceus*). A native of Malaya and Sumatra, this bird resembles and has the same habits as the Crested Argus of Annam.

The male has huge, beautifully coloured wings in red, buff and black. The throat is buff; the head has a long black and white crest; underparts are black and white; face and neck are naked and blue; legs are red.

The female is brown with normal wings and tail. Very little is known about its habits in the wild.

Two eggs are laid and take twenty-four days to hatch. Chicks are easy to rear.

Bornean Great Argus (*Argusianus argus grayi*). In the male, the main body colour is grey with reddish underparts; the wings and mantle are black with whitish spots; the back is buff; the breast is chestnut; the back of the neck carries a thin hairy mane; the rest of the neck and head is blue; the crest is velvety black. The female is all-over brown and chestnut.

The habits of these birds are the same as other members of the species. They have been successfully imported and reared in Europe, but rarely.

CHEER PHEASANT (*Catreus wallichii*)

A native of the Himalaya Mountains, the Cheer pheasant is found up to 10,000 ft in coveys of a dozen or so. The general body colour of the male is brown, black, buff and grey; the face and wattles are crimson. In shape it is much like the common pheasant. The female is much the same colour as the male but somewhat paler.

These birds are easy to rear but they cannot tolerate dampness. The eggs, twelve to sixteen in number, are flecked with reddish blotches on a cream background; they take twenty-seven days to incubate.

The Cheer pheasant is monogamous in the wild. They are ground birds, sleeping on the ground and rarely flying. Unlike most pheasants they live on live food, i.e. insects, mice, lizards and even small finches; in the wild they never eat green food. The Cheer pheasant is plentiful in aviaries in Europe and America.

ELLIOT PHEASANT (*Syrmaticus ellioti*)

This is also a long-tailed pheasant. It is a native of Eastern China. In the male, the head is mostly grey with a brown crown; the neck is black at the front; the underlying body colour is chestnut; mantle and wings are red; the lower breast and underparts are white; the tail coverts, flanks and thighs are chestnut, grey and black. The female is a dull brown, flecked with grey and black.

Six cream coloured eggs are laid and take twenty-five days to hatch.

Elliots are now scarce in Europe since they were lost during the last war, and the main stock around Woburn was decimated by the hard winter of 1947. I found them very tame and trusting but never succeeded in rearing any.

MIKADO (*Syrmaticus mikado*)

A native of Formosa, this bird lives at an altitude of 5000 to 8000 ft, in dense forests. It was discovered in 1911, after its tail feathers were found in the head-dress of a native.

The body of the male is purplish black; the head is dark blue; wings and tail are black with white bars; the mantle and breast are purplish black and blue; the underparts are black. In fact the whole bird's colouring is made up of a mixture of blue, purple, and black, the feathers having whitish tips.

The female is greenish brown flecked with black and white spots.

The eggs are cream coloured and several clutches may be laid in a season. They take twenty-seven days to incubate, the young reaching full plumage in five months.

In the wild the birds live mostly on green food and are very hardy.

Specimens in my aviaries were tame and easy to manage but the eggs were always infertile.

MELANISTIC MUTANT (*Phasianus tenebrosus*)

A mutation is the inception of a heritable variety. How it occurs is obscure and unknown. This one occurred spontaneously and simultaneously in England and Ireland about 1919, but it was probably in existence many years before then. (Some were discovered on Lord Rothschild's estate in 1880). It is unlikely that the inheritance comes from both parents since a mutation only occurs once in half a million. Although a Japanese, Negauietu Kuroda, in 1935, claimed that he obtained Phasianus tenebrosus by crossing the Chinese Ringneck with the Versicolor, my own experimental crossings produced progeny like ordinary Game pheasants in the first generation.

Figure 4

Elliot Pheasant
Cheer Pheasant
Kolass Pheasant
Monol Pheasant
Silver Pheasant

This mutation could be a reversion to an old type of several thousand years ago or it may have been originally due to a chromosome abnormality or a gene mutation, in which instance it will be reproduced in its new form.

Another theory is that the species may be descendants of a cross a great many years ago between the Game pheasant and the Black grouse. They cross readily and the progeny is fertile. The Black grouse was introduced into Ireland in 1899; it never became acclimatised and it is now extinct there. It is now found only in a few localities in the south-west of England, i.e. Somerset, Cornwall, Devon and Dorset. In Scotland and northern England, the Black grouse was shot to the point of extinction and there are now few breeding records.

I saw my first mutant when I visited an estate in County Kildare, where some 300 pheasants were being reared. In a field of normal coloured birds a single one was very noticeable for its different appearance. It was a dark chocolate brown with white tips to its wings and tail. I was assured by the Keeper that no mutant stock had been caught up for egg production and this was the only one of its type. It was a male, and when half grown I added it to my collection. At about this time I was lucky enough to obtain a female from another source. They bred fairly true; one normal coloured chick appeared in ten. The female had all the appearance of a red grouse but was slightly larger. People who saw these birds for the first time could not place their species.

The male is smaller than the other Game pheasants. The breast and mantle have a beautiful flashing iridescent plumage of purple, green and violet, continually changing with position and intensified by refraction of light in the feather structure. The body is metallic green; the wings and underparts are dark olive; the head and neck are purple; the facial skin is crimson; there is no white neck-ring. The female is dark chocolate brown with lighter markings. The number of eggs, colour and incubation period is similar to the other true pheasants.

WHITE PHEASANT

White pheasants occur frequently in the wild. They may be dark-eyed or red-eyed; if the latter, they are albinos. They are good aviary birds, but they are delicate to rear and if albinos, they have bad sight. The albino form is sex-linked and follows Mendelian laws accurately in all aspects such as colour, size, type and behaviour. Albinism is due to a genetical factor and there is no known cause why it should occur.

The following table shows breeding results:

1. Albino cock × albino hen = all albino cocks and hens.
2. Albino cock × normal hen = all albino hens and normal coloured cocks carrying the albino factor.
3. Normal coloured cock × albino hen = normal coloured cocks carrying the albino factor and normal coloured hens.
4. Normal coloured cock carrying the albino factor × normal coloured hen = 25% albino hens, 25% normal coloured cocks carrying the albino factor and the remainder all normal coloured cocks and hens.
5. Normal coloured cock carrying the albino factor × albino hen = albino cocks, albino hens, normal coloured cocks carrying the albino factor and normal coloured hens.

Two years ago I obtained a white, dark-eyed, ring-neck hen which was caught up in the wild. I mated her to a normal coloured male ring-neck. Of twenty-four eggs laid I reared eighteen birds to maturity. They were all normal coloured. The following year I mated the hen to one of her sons and of ten chicks reared, three were pure white. During two incubations the hen never left the nest except possibly, but improbably, during the hours of darkness. I have now established a strain of pure white birds which are really beautiful. The male is especially so since the white is enhanced by the crimson facial colouring. Peculiarly their eggs are sapphire blue whereas the normal colour pheasant's egg is from olive to pale green.

Figure 5   ELLIOT'S PHEASANTS
(*Gallophasis Ellioti*).

CHAPTER 4

VARIETIES OF PHEASANT: TWO

CROSSOPTILON (*Phasianus crossoptilon*)

Crossoptilons are members of the family of eared pheasants. They are natives of the great mountain ranges of Tibet and Southern China. They are unusual among pheasants in that male and female have similar colouring. There are seven sub-species all varying in plumage. The only one I have experience of is the Blue, i.e. *Crossoptilon auritum*. The top of the head in this bird is clothed in small, black, curly, velvety feathers; the ear coverts and throat are white; the facial skin is red; the general body plumage is bluish grey of a hairy appearance; the wing feathers are brown and the secondaries are purple. The most striking part is the tail, which differs from all other pheasants. It has twenty-four feathers and is shaped like the tail of a domestic fowl. The two upper central pairs, similar to ostrich plumes, are grey at the base, then change to green and purple at the ends. The outer or lower tail feathers are white at the base, with about two inches of the distal portion purple; the legs are red.

This species first came alive into Europe in 1929. Previous to this the bird's plumage was regularly imported for hat decoration. The difficulty of collecting specimens can be imagined, for the trappers had to walk through dense tropical jungle for months before reaching the haunts of this pheasant. The journey back to the markets of Shanghai and Burma also took months. The baskets of birds were carried by coolies, donkeys and river rafts on the Yangtze River. The carriers often had to wait several weeks for a caravan convoy with military escort, before travelling over bandit-ridden country. If they were caught, the pheasants were eaten and the men would have been lucky to get away with their own lives. In spite of all this and then a journey by steamer to Europe, they arrived in good condition. They immediately settled down and bred freely.

They are very tame in captivity and when reared on estates they will not wander.

Six brown eggs are laid and they take twenty-four days to hatch. The Crossoptilon is monogamous.

Other forms of the eared pheasant are the Szechuan White-eared; the Yuccan White-eared; the Tibetan White-eared; Dolans; Harmans and the Brown-eared. They all have similar habits.

TRAGOPAN

The genus Tragopan or horned pheasants includes probably some of the most beautiful birds on earth. There are five species. The males of each species are noted for the two fleshy horns and an apron-like skin, which in the breeding season swells, giving the bird a weird, colourful appearance. All Tragopans are monogamous.

Tragopans sometimes nest in trees in old nests of other large birds. The chicks' wings are fully developed and enclosed in sheaths when they leave the shell. The sheaths are immediately discarded and the chicks can then fly, being only a couple of hours old.

Satyr Tragopan (*Tragopan satyra*) is found at an altitude of from 6000 to 10,000 ft in forests in the Himalayas.

In the male the general body colouring is crimson; the head is black; the back is red with white spots, each spot being enclosed in a circle of black; the shoulders, breast and underparts are crimson; the tail coverts are red with black markings; the scapulars and wing coverts are brown, flecked with red; the wings and tail are buff and brown; the bare throat skin is light blue; two fleshy horns, blue in colour, protrude 2 in. long from the head. A bright blue fleshy bib covers the chest during the breeding season, adornments which then disappear for the remainder of the year.

Figure 6

Blue Crossoptilon
Mikado Pheasant
Satyr Tragopan
Versicolor Pheasant

J. Fitzsimons.

The female is brown with black and buff markings. Four eggs, cream coloured with red blotches, take twenty-eight days to incubate.

I found Satyrs very tame.

Timmincks Tragopan (*Tragopan timmerincki*) is a native of Burma, Tibet and Western China. Owing to intensive trapping it is becoming extinct. It is rarely imported. In the male, the naked throat skin with bib and head horns, like those of the Satyr Tragopan, are bright blue; the head is black; the crest, neck, breast and back are orange red; the rump is crimson; underparts are light crimson, with grey spots; the wings are light brown; the legs are red; the bill is black. The female is dark brown.

Timmincks are very hardy and can stand the severest winters. They cannot tolerate great heat, their natural habitat being dense, wet, shaded forests. Eggs and incubation period are the same as the Satyr and the chicks fly almost immediately after hatching.

Western Tragopan (*Tragopan melanocephalus*). This is a very rare species and it is doubtful if any live specimens can be found in Europe or America.

The body colour in the male is black, grey, buff, red and white; the neck is red; the tail is buff with black bars; underparts are black; the bare face skin is crimson; the throat is blue; the blue fleshy horns are like the other species. The female is grey and black with white streaks.

Blyth's Tragopan (*Tragopan blythi*) is a native of Burma and Assam.

In the male the head is mainly black; the crest, neck and breast are orange red; the body is black, brown and red; underparts are grey; facial skin is yellow and the horns are bright blue; the legs are pale red. The female is mainly brown with dark and whitish spots.

They live in dense forests up to 6000 ft. They were first imported into Europe 100 years ago and several have been bred in aviaries since then.

Cabot's Tragopan (*Tragopan caboti*) is a native of Eastern China. The body is buff, red and black; the bare throat skin is orange.

Their habits are similar to those of the other Tragopans. Their habitat is up to 5000 ft. They live mainly in trees at a great height where they also make their nests, usually laying their eggs in old nests of other birds.

KALIJS (*Kalijs gennaeus*)

All the Kalijs are coloured in silver and black with crests, red faces, red wattles and curved tails. They are all natives of the Himalayas, Assam, Burma, Siam, Indo- and Southern China. Intermediate coloured birds are sometimes found, which are probably hybrids.

There are two divisions; the first, the Blackbacked Kalij, has grey legs. There are nine sub-species of the Blackbacked, i.e. White Crested; Black Crested; Black Breasted; the Black Kalij; Hosfields; Williams; Oates, Lineated and Sharps. The second division consists of the Silver pheasant with red legs. There are eight sub-species, i.e. Rippons, Hainau, Berlioz, Bels, Aunamese, Lewis, Rubymines and the best known of all, the True Silver pheasant. The latter is the only one dealt with here.

Silver Pheasant (Gennaeus nycthemerus). This bird is a native of Indo-China, Southern China and the north western Himalayas. It is beautifully dressed, the back and wings are silvery white; the tail is arched and hangs in silvery sprays; the crest is pur-plish black; the face and legs are crimson. It is a most flam-boyant bird.

The female is dull brown with red legs.

Eggs are pinkish brown and take twenty-six days to hatch—several may be laid. The chicks are very easily reared.

Silver pheasants can be very wicked; attacking fiercely they can inflict severe injuries to children or adults with their sharp needle-like spurs. My own specimen is particularly vicious. If one enters his aviary he approaches slowly and stealthily, keeping up an incessant chattering. He then suddenly springs at the face with legs working like pistons, his spurs tearing the air and hitting with wings and beak. My bird attendant uses a forked stick to keep him off when feeding and cleaning. Strange to say he is quite docile with other male pheasants; this is in marked contrast to the Golden and Amherst, who, while very tame and friendly, will fight to the death of one in a few minutes if left together in the same enclosure. Many Silvers enjoy freedom on large estates without being inclined to wander as others do. They are liable to attack men at work.

LADY AMHERST (*Chrysolophus amherstiae*)

The Lady Amherst pheasant is named after its discoverer. Its natural habitat is Tibet, Southern China and Northern Burma, where it lives at an altitude of several thousand feet.

This is truly a magnificent and stately bird and next to the Golden it is the most popular. It is an ideal aviary specimen, happy and contented, and very tame. When displaying, the male shows off his gorgeous colouring to the best advantage. He spreads his mantle and cape, drops one wing stiffly and with tail downwards and spread, he takes short runs and then stays perfectly still. This goes on for hours and the female takes no notice. Very little is known of their habits in the wild state. In Europe they have been released on large estates and did fairly well at liberty. At Woburn Abbey in Bedfordshire several purebred Lady Amherst can be seen roaming over the grounds. I saw some Lady Amherst/Ringneck hybrids feeding with Ringnecks. The pure Lady Amhersts seemed to keep to themselves on a different part of the estate and did not mix with the other variety.

In the male the upper breast, back and mantle are bluish green; the lower breast is white; the rump is scarlet; legs are slate colour; the crest is crimson; the neck cape is whitish grey with dark bars; the long tail feathers are barred blue and black with four scarlet feathers on either side. No pigment can equal the brilliant colouring of this bird.

The female is dull brown with grey legs and face skin. The buff-coloured eggs take twenty-three days to hatch and up to thirty may be laid in a season. Chicks are very easy to rear and they are very hardy. The male does not reach adult plumage until he is one year old and is not fertile for two years.

Figure 7
Lady Amherst Pheasant
Edward's Pheasant
Timmincks Tragopan
Siamese Fireback

J. Fitzsimons

J.F.SIMMONS.

PEACOCK PHEASANT

Of the genus Polyplectron, there are twenty sub-species of the Peacock pheasant distributed over the Himalayas, Burma, Siam, Assam, Indo-China and Hainau. They live from sea level to 6000 ft in dense damp forests. They are very shy and are rarely seen in the wild. They are monogamous. They are in full plumage and fertility in two years. The females are smaller than the males and have a duller colouring. Only a few species have been imported.

Great Northern or Grey Peacock Pheasant (Polyplectron bicalcaratum). This bird is no bigger than a pigeon. In the male, the general body plumage is steel grey with numerous white spots and scattered green, purple and violet ocelli. There are four sub-species, differing in colour according to locality. The female is grey with dark purple markings.

A peculiarity of this pheasant is that it lays only two cream coloured eggs and the young are fed by regurgitation of food by the mother, as in the case of the pigeon. The chicks will not pick food from the ground until they are several days old.

When displaying, the male is like a miniature peacock. When the feathers vibrate the ocelli seem to revolve at an enormous speed, giving the bird a weird uncanny appearance. It breeds well in captivity and is now numerous in America and Europe.

Germain Peacock Pheasant (Polyplectron germaini) is a native of Annam and Cochin China. It is similar in colouring and habits to the Great Northern, but there is more purple in the plumage. It lives in dense forests up to 4000 ft. It is not so hardy as other members of the family and the chicks are difficult to rear. Eggs are creamy white and incubation takes twenty-two days. It is well established in the U.S.A.

Hainan Peacock Pheasant (Polyplectron katsumatae). This pheasant is smaller and of much the same colouring, but darker than the others. It has never been imported alive.

Figure 8

Rheinhart's Argus
Peacock Pheasant
Mongolian Pheasant
Peacock

Malay Peacock Pheasant (Polyplectron malacensis). This bird has a long purple greenish crest; large blue ocelli are distributed on the back and tail; face skin is orange; feet and bill are grey.

This is a native of Malaya and Sumatra. The first pair arrived in Europe 100 years ago. Several have since been imported but they did not live long, the climate being too cold.

Sumatran Bronzetail Peacock Pheasant (Chalcurus chalcurus). A native of Sumatra, the male of this pheasant is mostly brown, barred with black. The female is similar in colouring. It stands importation well. It is a good aviary bird and breeds freely. Two white eggs take twenty-two days to hatch.

Palawar Peacock Pheasant or Napoleon Pheasant (Polyplectron amphanum). This bird is found only on the island of Palowar, between Borneo and the Philippines. It is really one of the most beautiful birds in existence and is one of the smallest of the pheasants.

In the male the crown of the head and crest are green; the neck is black; the mantle and wings are bright blue, tinged with green; the back is golden buff; the tail is buff with bright green markings. The female is dull brown. Creamy white eggs take eighteen days to hatch.

This pheasant has been freely imported into Europe where it breeds well in aviaries. It does not like cold and should, if possible, have a heated shelter. Males do not reach full plumage for three years. For successful rearing chicks must have live food.

FIREBACKS

Firebacks belong to a large family of gallo pheasants which include Kalijs, Blue pheasants and Wattled pheasants. They inhabit the jungles of Malaya, Borneo, Annam, Sumatra and Indo-China. They all resemble each other in shape and habits. There are two species without head crests and six with head crests. All are beautifully coloured in silver, purple, black, red, cobalt and maroon; the colour blending according to locality.

Bornean Crestless Fireback (Acomus pyronotus (Beebe)). This pheasant is a native of Borneo. It lives along the coast around Sarawak. Little is known of its habits in the wild. It has been imported into Europe but never bred in captivity.

Its general body colour is purplish black; the tail is buff; the neck is grey with white streaks; tail coverts are blue; the rump is maroon. The female is chestnut brown.

Malayan Crestless Fireback (Acomus erythrophthalmus (Beebe)). This pheasant is a native of Malaya and Sumatra and frequents the jungles. It takes to aviary life in Europe better than other members of its family and it is easily reared. It has been freely imported over the last fifty years. The male bird has a white tail which is the only difference between it and the Bornean; it has no crest. In the male the face is scarlet; neck and throat are bluish black; the body is maroon and purple; underparts are black. Young are fully coloured in six months. The female is black with a brownish head. Four eggs take twenty-four days to incubate.

Siamese Crested Fireback (Lophura diardi (Beebe)). This pheasant is a native of Indo-China and lives in dense jungle forests. It is a strikingly handsome bird, being easily the most magnificent of its family. In the male, the head is black with a bright blue crest; the main body colour is grey, flecked with purplish black; the back is flaming gold; the rump is red; face wattles are crimson; the lower back and tail covert feathers are steel blue with crimson fringes; the underparts are black.

The female is brown, flecked with black and white.

The males acquire adult plumage their first year but are not fertile until they are three years old. They do well in large aviaries, but in close confinement the male may murder his mate. About six buff coloured eggs are laid and take twenty-four days to incubate.

Lesser Bornean Crested Fireback (Lophura ignita (Beebe)). This pheasant is a native of Borneo. In this bird the main body colour is purplish blue; the face wattles are blue; the head, crest, neck, mantle, breast and back are purplish blue; the tail feathers are maroon and black; the beak is white, iris red; the legs are grey. The female is chestnut and black.

These birds are very delicate and are difficult to keep alive out of their native country. Six white eggs take twenty-four days to incubate.

Other Crested Firebacks are the Greater Crested, Bornean Crested, Vieillots and Delacours.

THE WHITE TAILED WATTLED PHEASANT *(Loprophasis bulweri).*
A native of Borneo, this is noted for its wonderful white tail of thirty-two feathers, which it spreads open in a vertical circle. It has never been imported.

BLOOD PHEASANTS *(Ithaginis)*

Blood pheasants belong to the genus *Ithaginis.* There are thirteen sub-species, all of the same habits and body shape. They are natives of Northern China, Burma, Tibet, Nepal, Central Asia. They live higher than any other pheasant, being found only in mountain ranges near the snow line from 9000 to 15,000 ft.

Colouring in the different sub-species varies greatly, but the general shades are black, buff, grey, green, crimson, yellow and brown of varying distribution in the different sub-species; which are the Himalayan, Tibetan, Clarkes, Vernay's, Greenway's, Geoffroy's, Biandu's and Berozowski's. There are many intermediate forms, probably the result of hybridising. Being acclimatised to high altitudes they will not live at sea level. They have been imported alive into Europe, but they did not live long and have never bred. About ten speckled brown eggs are laid on the ground. The birds rarely fly except to roost.

MONOL PHEASANTS *(Lophophorus)*

Of the genus *Lophophorus,* these pheasants are distributed throughout the Himalayas, Afghanistan and Western China, in open forests from 6000 to 15,000 ft.

There are three species which are covered below. No words can describe their brilliant colouring of red, purple, green, blue and gold. They are very hardy and breed freely in aviaries, where they live up to twenty-five years. They are polygamous. They lay about eight cream coloured eggs, flecked with brown. They cross freely with domestic poultry, but the progeny is sterile. Their call is a long, low, piercing whistle.

Impeyan Pheasant (Lophophorus impeyanus). This bird, discovered by Sir Elijah and Lady Impey, is also known as the Himalayan Monol and is the best known of the species. It lives up to 12,000 ft. It is a really beautiful, stately pheasant, very hardy and easy to rear if fertile eggs are obtainable. Often a pair put together for the first time will not agree; the male may murder his mate.

If one can get a pair on good terms, the rest is easy. Of all pheasants this is one of the most wonderfully coloured.

In the male, the head and crest are a brilliant green; the mantle is iridescent green; the throat and underparts are black; the neck is green and red; the back and wings are a blended green, violet and blue; the tail is reddish brown. The female is light brown with dark brown mottling.

Sclater's Monol (*Lophophorus sclateri*) is a native of Burma, Assam and Tibet, in forests up to 10,000 ft. The colouring is much the same as that of the Impeyan, but distributed differently. The face is green; ear coverts are blue; neck is copper colour; wing coverts and mantle are green, purple and maroon; underparts are black; tail is rusty brown; bill is yellow; legs are green.

The female is brown and black. The throat is white; the bill is yellow; the legs are brown and spurred.

Chinese Monol (*Lophophorus lhuysi*). The general body colour is black, green, purple, maroon, white and blue. The female is mainly dark brown with white throat. Only a few specimens have been imported alive.

IMPERIAL PHEASANT (*Gennaeus imperialis* (*Beebe*))

This pheasant is very rare and has seldom been obtained. A native of Annam and Quangtri, the bird lives in deep forests and inaccessible mountains. The only pair taken to Europe alive bred well and laid the foundation of stocks now breeding freely in America. Nothing is known of its habits in the wild.

Its general body colour is blue; the wing coverts are brown with black markings; the face is crimson and the blue head carries a dark blue crest.

The female is mainly brown.

KOLASS PHEASANT (*Pucrasia*)

The Kolass pheasants belong to the genus Pucrasia. They are natives of the Himalayas, Tibet, Northern and Eastern China, in very high altitudes at from 4000 to 15,000 ft. in deep forests. They travel in pairs, being strictly monogamous and staying together for life. They have been bred in Europe, but they are very delicate and difficult to keep alive. They nest on the ground. Six buff eggs with reddish spots are laid. They reach full plumage and are fertile in one year.

Common Kolass (Pucrasia macrolopha macrolopha). This bird was first introduced into Europe about eighty years ago. It is a native of the mountains of China. In the male the body colour is mainly black, green, white and buff; the head carries a four inch red crest and velvety black ear tufts five inches long; the bill is black and the legs are blue. The head is fully feathered in both the male and female.

Other members of the genus are the Punjab Kolass, the Kashmir, the Western, Nepal, Meyers, Orange collared, Yellow necked and Darwins.

EDWARD'S PHEASANT *(Gennaeus edwardi)*

This pheasant is a native of the mountains of Annam. Edwards are forest dwellers, and are never seen outside dense humid jungle, at altitudes of up to 4000 ft. In captivity they are hardy and easy to rear. Fortunately, they are now plentiful in aviaries in Europe and America.

The main body colour in the male is dark silky blue; the wings are light blue with black primaries; the tail is blue; the head has a white cap; the face and legs are crimson; the iris is dark red; the bill is ivory. The female is dull brown. Eggs, six in number, take twenty-two days to incubate.

These birds reach full adult plumage the first year but are not fertile until they are two years old.

PRINCE OF WALES PHEASANT *(Phasianus principalis)*

This pheasant was discovered comparatively recently. It is a native of the Afghan Frontier of India, Turkestan, and Afghanistan. In the male, the head and crown are green; the neck is maroon; the body colour is metallic brown all over. Little is known of its habits in its native habitat.

CHAPTER 5

ASSOCIATED SPECIES

Peafowl

There are two species of peafowl, the Blue Indian (*Pavo cristatus*), and the Specifer or Burmese peafowl (*Pavo muticus*). There are two mutations of the Blue, i.e. the White and the Blackshouldered. The Blue is found only in India, Ceylon and Assam, in tropical jungle up to 6000 ft, where nature produces its most brilliantly coloured birds and flowers.

The Peacock is the most brilliant of all. He is lavishly adorned in green, blue, purple, lavender, gold, bronze, orange, black and grey. He takes pride in showing off his marvellous train as he raises and lowers it and spreads it, to allow the sun's rays to play with it and reveal its glorious colours. "As proud as a Peacock", is an old and true saying.

In the days of Emperor Alexander they were a great delicacy and they were regularly roasted for banquets. The tongues were reserved for Royalty. They were imported and kept at the Court of Solomon who, in his wisdom to please his Queen, showed her his "fine cloth, tapestries, embroideries, precious stones, gold, silver, spices, ivory and peacocks."

In Europe, Blue Indian Peacocks, like pheasants are easy to keep. They like to be near running water and cultivated land. They are not suitable for aviaries, for in close confinement they tend to break or soil their tails; a peacock with a broken tail sulks and hides as if ashamed to appear in public.

Peacocks are best kept in a high walled garden containing high trees for perching. One drawback is their appetite for flowers. Although some varieties of flowers will at first appear to have no attraction, sooner or later they will all be taken. Another drawback is that they are very noisy. They are great weather prophets, crying aloud on the approach of rain. In their natural state, peafowl feed on grain, a variety of green food, fruit buds and all sorts of insects and small animals, such as lizards, mice and frogs. They are polygamous, one male running with up to five females. They lay up to twelve eggs and incubation is twenty-eight days. Chicks are best hatched and reared by a turkey. The nest is similar to that of a pheasant. The young are not mature or in full plumage until they are three years old.

Burmese peafowl come from Siam, Indo-China, Sumatra and Malaya. They are more beautifully coloured than the Blue, but they are not so hardy and cannot stand frosts. They are not suited to our climate.

Jungle Fowl

Jungle fowl are the ancestors of all modern breeds of domestic poultry. They became domesticated about 1300 B.C. The culture was started by the Chinese, and selection has now produced hundreds of different varieties. They are polygamous, and scratchers and diggers like pheasants.

There are four species of jungle fowl and several sub-species:

1. The Red Jungle fowl (*Gallus gallus*) the ancestor of our domestic poultry. It is a native of India, Southern China, Malaya, Java and Indo-China.
2. The Ceylon (*Gallus lafayetti*), a native of Ceylon. It is delicate and rarely imported.
3. The Java or Green (*Gallus varius*), is a native of Java. This species cannot live in our climate. It is the most beautiful of all.
4. The Grey (*Gallus somerati*), is a native of India; it has been bred in Europe, but it is not hardy.

In shape, colouring, habits, feeding and reproduction, jungle fowl are very similar to their domestic relatives. The nearest approach would be our red game fowl. The hens are extremely quarrelsome among themselves and will fight to the death if confined in close quarters.

Hybrids

Pheasants hybridise with other gallinaceous species already mentioned. The hybrid produced by crossing with domestic fowl is known as a pero and it has sometimes been fertile. I obtained two specimens from Mr Potterton of Carbury, County Kildare, who bred them freely from a wild caught up male and a Rhode Island Red hen. Both were males and both had only one eye; both had the pheasant head and tail and the body shape and reddish plumage of a Rhode Island hen. Since then I bred several specimens myself. They all had the fowl characteristics except for the colouring which was mostly that of the pheasant. I heard of a hybrid which had one pheasant leg with a large spur and one smaller leg without a spur. Hybrids between the pheasant and domestic poultry are usually of a dull drab colour and are not much to be admired. There are records of a pheasant turkey cross, also of a cross with guinea fowl.

Some hybrids among pheasants are really beautiful, the colouring is outstanding. The loveliest is probably the Golden Amherst cross, which carries all the colours of the male of each parent species.

The Silver pheasant crosses freely with the Golden, Reeves, Firebacks, and Game pheasants and the males may be fertile.

The Game pheasant will hybridise with the Golden, Reeves, Amherst and Silver.

While infertile among themselves, hybrids may be fertile when crossed with other pheasants or domestic fowl. They are not mules, which are completely barren.

There is little motive in breeding hybrids, for ideally all varieties of pheasants should be kept pure. However, if surplus birds, cocks or hens, are without mates, then you can try crossing just for curiosity. While many species of pheasants and other birds will hybridise in captivity they never will in the wild, even though closely related. Nature arranged this.

Megapodes (*Lipoa megapodiiae*)

The Megapodiiae or Mound birds are a small but most remarkable family of birds, distantly related to pheasants. The largest member of the family is the Brush Turkey, *Tallegallus lathami*, which is the size of a small hen turkey; the bird is a native of Northern Australia. The head and neck are bare and the skin is bright red finishing in a bright yellow wattle; the body colour is sooty brown.

The strange thing about this bird is its method of incubating its eggs. The female lays them in a heap of decaying vegetable matter and hot sand. The eggs are placed upright on the pointed end and never turned; the heat generated hatches them. The young can fly almost immediately after they leave the shell.

NATIVE PHEASANT (*Lipoa acellata*)

This member of the family of Megapodiiae is also known as the Native Pheasant or Mallee Bird, the place name of its habitat in Northern Australia. It is also found in the Islands of Samoa, the Tonga group, New Guinea, the Philippines and neighbouring islands. These birds were first described by Gould. They have crested brown heads; short tails; long red legs and large feet; the body colour is a mixture of grey, brown, black, white and buff.

Mallee Birds also are mound builders. Some lay their eggs in holes in sand on the beaches like the turtle. Others build mounds or tumuli of sand and vegetable matter usually in the shade of a tree. The mound is sometimes up to 15 ft high and 60 ft in circumference; it is carefully laid down by the male and into it are packed leaves, grasses, sticks, and rotting timber. Everything is scratched into the mound backwards by one foot, while the bird stands on the other.

When a pile is set up it is then covered with sand. Decomposition and fermentation now set in and the temperature rises. When it reaches the correct degree, the female starts to lay several eggs in holes two to three feet in the mound which have been opened specially on each occasion by the male. When the egg is laid the male covers it over with sand immediately. The male's duty is to see that the temperature is kept right: if the mound becomes too hot the eggs will cook, so he removes sand to allow it to cool. If the temperature drops he covers it up hurriedly with more sand to prevent loss of heat. When fermentation has ceased and there is no heat formation from within, he again rises to the occasion: he opens up the whole mound completely for the mid-day sun to warm it; before the sun goes down the mound is closed up again so that the heat is retained for the night. The temperature is tested by the birds thrusting their beaks into the mound.

Another member of the family wears a large remarkable helmet-like fleshy growth, on the back of its head. Like the neck, it is bare and of a crimson colour; the body plumage is purplish black and the underparts are flamingo red. It has the same incubation habits as the Brush Turkey and the Mallee Bird.

Figure 9   LADY AMHERST PHEASANTS
(*Thaumalea Amherstiæ*).

CHAPTER 6

FEEDING AND LAYING DOWN STOCK

Feeding Chicks

The feeding of pheasant chicks, whether they are game, or of
the ornamental varieties, is exactly the same. All pheasant
breeders claim to have a never failing formula for feeding; they
are all more or less correct. Over the years I have tried all sorts
of mixtures and the one I now use has never failed.

For the first few days I use raw egg, yolk and white, one egg
to twelve chicks, mixed with a variety of finely chopped green
food, lettuce, spinach, dandelion, chickweed, onion tops and a
little dried milk powder and a trace of glucose. Before mixing,
the hands should be smeared with cod liver oil. Fine biscuit
meal and custard can be fed as a change. Hard boiled egg, in
my opinion, is very indigestible.

At this time the mother hen is very hungry and she will eat all
the food; she should therefore be given oats; the chicks will not
touch them. In about three days when the egg tooth is shed, a
little pinhead oatmeal should be added to the mixture. After
a week white millet should be added, together with a very little
plain canary seed and very fine grit. A stock mixture can be
made up containing pinhead oatmeal 7 lb, milk powder 1 lb,
a packet of wheatgerm proprietary baby food, $\frac{1}{2}$ oz glucose,
$\frac{1}{4}$ lb white millet and $\frac{1}{4}$ lb canary seed. At feeding time a few
handfuls of this should be added to a mass of finely chopped
green food, mixed, and the raw egg added. It will be found that
all the green food and other ingredients are eaten first and the
pinhead oatmeal last of all. Later on boiled rice is appreciated
and a little boiled potato and minced beef may be added.
Boiled minced rabbit is a great standby.

Although the most important item is green food, of which
chicks consume enormous quantities, live food is also of value
but can be done without if unobtainable; chicks that get it

thrive better than others. In the wild they obtain a variety of soft insects for the first few days. Afterwards they feed on hard-shelled beetles when they are strong enough to break them up. A good way of supplying live food is to obtain some rotting meat or offal from the butcher. This is placed on a sieve or close mesh wire, or a large box or tea chest half filled with sand or granulated peat. The bluebottle lays her eggs on the meat and as the resulting maggots mature they drop into the box, burrow down, clean themselves and form cocoons; there is nothing chicks like better.

Chicks should not be fed for thirty-six hours after hatching. During this time they live on their own yolk sac, which is being absorbed and digested. Clean warm water must be given immediately and for want of a better receptacle an inverted jam jar on a saucer can be used.

Up to forty-eight hours old, in a healthy chick, the motion is black, white and green; if there is no white the chick is ailing and will live only a few days.

When the birds are three weeks old, green food can be fed in a bunch without chopping, or lettuce by the head. It should be kept down by a stone to prevent it being dragged around. Better still, it may be hung up to force the birds to jump for it. It is imperative to cut off the roots with the earth attached to prevent a gapeworm-infected earthworm from being introduced.

At six weeks, wheat, barley, hemp, fish and meat meal, and a meat bone to pick may be given, also raw grated carrot and fruit.

The golden rule of little and often is not easy to carry out. Some rearers give the first meal at daybreak—I find that to leave enough for the morning with the night feed suffices. Some approve of dry feeding, some wet or mash feeding—the ideal is some of each. For busy people who cannot afford a great deal of time, dry feeding is the easiest. Many excellent proprietary foods are on the market and they can be very successful, but they are not so good as the green food mixture. Hoppers with small holes should be used so that the food cannot be scattered on the ground and become soiled.

Chicks fed on foods containing antibiotics grow faster than they would otherwise do, possibly by arresting the activity of bacteria in the intestinal tract which, though not lethal, may retard growth.

For those who prefer labour saving foods, Turkey Starter Crumbs are recommended. The high protein content ensures rapid progress.

Feeding Adults

The staple diet of adult birds in captivity is grain of various kinds and only enough of it for a quick meal. Hoppers filled with a dry proprietary domestic fowl meal should always be left in the shelter with clean water and grit. As well as this, kitchen scraps, soaked bread, potatoes and various cooked vegetables may be offered; they must be fresh and never sour. Green food such as cabbages in variety and lettuce should be hung in the aviary, and all kinds of fruit and non-poisonous berries may be given. Birds relish a meat bone to pick. If it is desired to gain a pheasant's confidence, give it a few currants and raisins.

Feeding in the Wild

In the wild, game pheasants' food consists of fruit, nuts, berries, rose hips, haws, ivy berries, privet, green food, grain, weed seeds, insects and their grubs, leather-jackets, earth-worms, mice, tubers of buttercup, beech mast and acorns. They consume enormous quantities of the click or skipjack beetle, which is the adult of the destructive wireworm; 1200 of the latter have been found in a pheasant's crop.

Laying Down Stock

When catching up pheasants in an enclosure a net is essential; an ordinary trout net with a handle 4 to 5 ft long is ideal and the birds can be caught quickly and without harm. When caught, they should be held by the legs with the body resting in the left arm, their feathers should be stroked and they should be reassured by speaking gently to them; they will stay perfectly still. A pheasant should never be caught by chasing it around the enclosure and cornering it; it becomes terrified and most likely will damage itself. If birds are going to travel a distance they should be packed in roomy boxes without any draughts and with no delay in transit. Birds should never be packed if they are wet, following rain.

When laying down stock the terrain must be considered. Game pheasants like wooded country, especially oak with heavy undergrowth near running water, convenient to tillage, or else in tall grasses or reeds and near where they can get their natural food.

Pheasants rarely fly except to roost in trees in winter. In other seasons they prefer to sleep in long grass, rushes or swamp reeds.

Releasing

The owner or renter of a shoot usually arrives with his hampers of pheasants; he tips them out in cover and expects them to stay put, happy and contented. In a few days he is astonished to find that they have disappeared. They may be several miles away from the point of release and they are probably still travelling until they find more suitable peaceful surroundings. The reason is simple. The catching up and transport fuss has terrified the birds and their one desire is for freedom and to get as far away from the terror as possible. One cannot say that a pheasant must be obliged to stay just where the owner wants it.

Before the birds arrive, a large wire-netting enclosure, size depending on the number, should be roughly erected near a wood or copse with good surrounding cover. Fir boughs should be placed inside to provide shelter and places to hide, together with a plentiful supply of grain and fresh water. Avoid "treated" corn which has been prepared to kill crows—this has been fed to birds by mistake. The birds should be released inside the enclosure by leaving the hamper lids open at night.

After two or three weeks without disturbance the birds will show signs of tameness; after dark the netting may then be quietly raised off the ground on one side for about 12 to 18 in.; the following morning the birds will walk out. They are now familiar with the surroundings; they will return to feed and roost for the night. Some will take to the trees and gradually they all will; at this time the structure can be completely removed and the birds will stay in the area. Liberal feeding should be maintained. Wild seeds and small corn discarded from the threshing mills should be thrown in dry ditches and undergrowth—under such conditions pheasants will not stray. If a piece of ground is conveniently available, it may be ploughed and sown with various kinds of corn, peas and beans and left uncut.

Figure 10   SŒMMERRING'S PHEASANTS
(*Phasianus sœmmerringii*).

(see "Copper Pheasant" in text)

CHAPTER 7

PHEASANT REARING

Covert Mating and Incubating

BEHAVIOUR IN THE WILD

In winter male and female pheasants segregate and remain in flocks until mid March. Like all birds, especially migrants, the male pheasant arrives first in early spring and selects the breeding territory. Daylight hours are increasing and more food can be obtained. With better feeding they put on weight, get fitter and reproduction is stimulated. The mating call then starts with a whirring of wings and a dance. Wing flapping is the reverse to that of the domestic fowl, the male of which flaps his wings first and crows afterwards; the pheasant crows first and then flaps his wings. This performance attracts the females who begin to gather around. If they like the terrain and the male they will stay; if not, they wander farther until they find more congenial surroundings.

Up to this time the male will have slowly wandered alone, stepping steadily and gracefully, but in April, after many fights with other males, he becomes attached to from five to ten females. The vanquished males, usually the very old, or very young, late hatched from the previous season, must remain celibate. The victor now assumes a more stately stance and with a defiant look, he struts around in a majestic manner. The cere and face become bright crimson; the crest feathers stand erect and the ears protrude. The call now becomes more frequent and is answered by the chosen females, who, like all wild birds, will only answer the call of their own mate. Display and courtship now starts; the wing next to the female drops, the head is bowed; the tail spread. The female seems completely bored and keeps on picking; she eventually stops and mating takes place. Coming on to the end of April and beginning of May, laying and hatching are in full swing and from then onwards the male takes no more interest in the proceedings. He takes no part in incubating or rearing.

REARING

The hen pheasant makes her nest on the ground, concealed in high grass or scrub. It is hollowed out and lined with grasses and leaves, with tints to suit the colour of the surroundings. In it she lays ten to twelve olive-coloured eggs. Sometimes two hens will lay in the same nest, or she may lay in the nest of a partridge or wild duck. Pheasants have been known to nest in trees or in an old nest of a crow, hawk or magpie. If her first effort is not successful she will lay a second or third clutch; nature arranges the brood numbers.

Birds subject to great mortality have the largest broods. If the pheasants laid only four or five eggs, as do most small birds, such as finches, blackbirds, thrushes, starlings, hawks, or crows, they would now be extinct or nearly so, since the mortality in the wild is always around 50 per cent before maturity is reached in ground-reared birds. Smaller birds have the protection of the nest up to the time they are fully fledged and can lead a separate existence and so avoid dangers.

CONTROLLED BREEDING

Game stock should be caught up in September, or October, so that they can be well settled down before breeding starts. Only the finest and most vigorous and early hatched birds should be selected; unhealthy stock should always be rejected. The birds need to be fed well on grain, green food, grit and clean water; hoppers must always be used and food never thrown on the ground. A new or breeding pen can be constructed of 2 in. mesh wire netting on dry, well-drained ground. It should be made as large as possible and it can be divided into as many compartments as required. It is as well to surround it outside, half way up, by wooden hoarding or sheets of galvanised iron; fir boughs may be arranged inside to provide cover. If possible, the attendants should always be the same so that the birds will get to know and to trust them.

The wings may be clipped and the birds released after the summer moult, or brails may be fitted to one wing; this is not necessary unless the enclosure is open at the top, and this has the additional disadvantage that wild males can fly in. The better way is to have the enclosure covered above and allow one male to run with four to six females. This is the best method when large quantities of eggs are required. If so many are not needed, they may be collected in the wild from first nests, leaving the hen to lay and rear a second clutch.

Eggs must be handled carefully; small, deformed or cracked eggs will not hatch; a good sized egg should weigh $1\frac{1}{10}$ oz. They should be stored on their sides in the sawdust, in a temperature not over 50° F. It is said that if eggs are stored on their ends, chicks will be deformed, but this is not correct. Stored eggs must be turned at least twice daily, otherwise chicks will be weak. Eggs should not be kept beyond ten days before setting, as fertility then begins to drop.

When enough eggs are collected, they should be set under several hens at the same time, then if there are bad hatches, clutches can be joined to make full ones. The hen then left without any chicks can take another setting of eggs. Bantams are the best for rearing; small hens will do but never a large heavy hen, for she will flatten and kill all the chicks as they leave the shell. If bantams are unobtainable, a stone as big as one's fist placed in the centre of the nest will keep the hen's body raised up. The older hens are the best; young ones may be very wild and they are not nearly as careful with chicks. Ten eggs to a small hen are sufficient. The body brood area, i.e. the area of breast stripped of feathers, must touch each egg when incubating. The hen leaves the nest once daily for food, exercise and toilet; during this time the eggs cool rapidly. The sitting hen turns her eggs every hour night and day. Eggs must be kept moist, otherwise the chicks cannot break through the tough membrane lining and shell. When chicks begin to hatch they tap out a crack around the egg, leaving one portion untouched to act as a hinge. They then kick the two portions of the shell apart and emerge.

The egg has two membranes; one surrounds the chick and one lines the inside of the shell. The chick should emerge from the egg at any time up to twelve hours after chipping. If the chick is in distress, which is evidenced by the egg being partly chipped for some hours and loud chirps and struggling going on inside, then the bird must be helped out by continuing the crack already made around half the egg with a sharp-pointed knife. It should then be left for an hour and if no further advance is made, the crack may be continued all the way round. If the chick still cannot work its way out, then the lid of the shell may be removed, and the head and neck only lifted out from under the wing where it is tucked in. The chick must be left in the shell and replaced in the nest incubator—it will then manage to release itself unless it is a weakling. Immediately chicks hatch they must be shut in their boxes with sacks thrown over, and next day transferred to the rearing field in coops on grass that has not been used for rearing any gallinaceous birds for at least three years.

Each coop should have a wire netting runout. They should be 20 ft apart and never placed in hot sun or under dripping trees. They should be away from cover that might hide predators. In ten to fourteen days, when chicks are strong enough, the runout can be removed and fir boughs left about the coup for shelter. When grass gets soiled coops should be moved to fresh ground. When doing so, the coop should be wrapped in fish netting, otherwise the chicks will play hide and seek. Handle chicks as little as possible. Coops are very easily constructed from a wooden box; laths can be nailed on the front 3 or 4 in. apart and a hinged or sliding door fitted at the side.

ARTIFICIAL INCUBATION

Artificial incubation is as old as civilisation itself—the ancient Egyptians incubated in kilns. Since then, many methods with various types of equipment have been used. Today, there are on the market up-to-date machines of all sizes to take up to 3000 eggs. The forced-air incubator seems to be more widely used now than the still-air incubator. A fair amount of experience is necessary with each machine at the beginning. Moisture and temperature recordings should be taken three or four times daily. If the first hatch is bad, it should be changed, until eventually a high percentage of live chicks is obtained. The manufacturers' instructions must be read very carefully. It is advisable to use only the best incubators and not to trust cheap ones. Incubators should be thoroughly disinfected after each hatch. It is best to start with a temperature of 95° F. and drop 3° each week, allowing fifteen to twenty minutes each day to cool the eggs. The eggs must be turned at least four times daily; if left for more than eight hours without turning, the embryo chick is liable to drop to the side of the shell and become attached to it, it cannot then hatch and if it does manage to, it may be a cripple. Eggs must be kept moist at all times, and light-tested every eight days—it is useless to try to hatch infertile eggs.

If disease is suspected in the parent stock, it is not advisable to breed from them unless circumstances force this, such as may happen when only one pair of very rare pheasants is owned; in this case, the eggs must be disinfected before setting. They should be washed in warm water and placed in a solution of citric acid, one part; warm water, three parts, for a few minutes. The eggs should then again be washed in warm water. It is not advisable to use this method when hatching under hens or the eggs will be squashed, for citric acid dissolves a slight part of the shell. Eggs may be dipped in calcium hypochlorite 1 per cent solution.

Aviaries

CONSTRUCTION OF AVIARIES

An aviary can be of any design or shape and should be as large as possible, but not greater than a 10 ft run. If too long, the birds, if they take flight, will gather too much impetus and kill themselves against the wire netting. The shelter should be about 6 ft × 5 ft or less, and about 7 ft high; it should face south, never north, and must be well lighted; a door is not necessary. If the shelter window is of glass it must be covered with wire netting in case the birds fly against it; strong perches must be provided inside and outside. Pheasants will always roost on the highest perch, so if it is desired to keep them indoors at night, it is wise to make the indoor perches higher than the outside ones. All floors should be made of concrete; following rain, grass runs become very muddy, especially if the occupants are diggers. My own pheasants never use the shelter except to eat and in wet weather; they prefer to sleep out even on the coldest nights.

Wire must be half-inch mesh to keep out rats and sparrows; the latter will eat all the food. Mice will get in anywhere but they will be pecked to death if they approach the food pot at the same time as a pheasant; if the mouse is a tiny one he may be swallowed alive. Wire should be sunk 12 in. in the ground to keep out burrowing animals. The framework can be of wood for cheapness; steel is better and will last for a lifetime, but it is much more expensive. Scrap iron piping is excellent. Framework timber and wire should be painted with a black leadless paint. The inside of the shelter should be limewashed.

Shrubs may be provided to make the enclosure look more attractive. They should be planted in tubs or boxes and they should be about 4 to 5 ft high, so that they cannot be trampled on; if too high, the pheasants will try to roost on them and break them down. The most suitable shrubs are Cupressus, Holly, Rhododendrons, all the Heaths, Bamboo, Elder, Birch, various Dwarf Conifers, Furze, Pampas Grass, Privet and Gooseberries. As well as improving the appearance of the aviary, they also afford protection to the females when the males are wicked. Laburnum, Ivy leaves and Rhus are poisonous and must be excluded.

As well as pheasants, various foreign birds, finches and canaries, can be kept in the same enclosure—they will all agree. A budgerigar likes nothing better than taking a ride on a pheasant's back, but it will destroy all the shrubs by chewing them. It is impossible to have growing shrubs and budgerigars in the same enclosure.

REARING IN AVIARIES

I use this method quite a lot, although one drawback is that one clutch of chicks will take up a whole enclosure which perhaps cannot be spared. If two lots of chicks are left to run together, while they will agree, the mothers will kill any others that do not belong to them. Bantams are vicious, jealous creatures and will not tolerate anything else in the same enclosure. However, in aviaries, chicks can be kept free from infectious diseases, predators and dozens of other dangers awaiting them.

The aviaries must be concreted and limewashed once weekly. A little non-poisonous disinfectant may be added to the limewash. The chicks must be removed to an adjoining aviary until the lime is dry, otherwise the birds may get lime in their eyes, which results in blindness no matter what treatment is given.

Arrangements with a box-like shelter and ½ in. wire netting runout are very successful and easy to handle. They are laid on grass and can be moved every day on to clean ground. The ground must be free from infection and it must not have been used for rearing for at least three years previously, as in a rearing field. The hen and brood can remain there for several weeks.

CAGE REARING

Of all the methods I tried, cage rearing is by far the best, simplest and easiest. Cages are constructed of ½ in. wire mesh on a wooden framework about 36 in. long, 18 in. high and 18 in. wide, with a door at the side. This size will hold up to ten chicks with the mother, although they can be made larger if desirable. If space is lacking, they can be built up in tiers in a bright, draughtproof shed or room.

Immediately chicks are hatched, they can be placed with the bantam in the cage, which has already been cleaned and disinfected. When the cage becomes soiled the birds can be driven out by the side door into another clean one. Chicks can remain in the cages until they are old enough to be independent of the mother. The latter is then removed and several clutches can be joined together and released into an aviary or other large enclosure. In cages they are protected from weather and are absolutely disease-free; not one bird should be lost. Cages can be left out during the day if weather is suitable and carried into the shed at night. If the latter is very bright and facing south, the cages need never be moved except for cleaning.

SEXING CHICKS

This is a most interesting study, brought to an art by the Japanese, where sexing chicks has been practised for many years. When the bird is a few hours old, the vent or rectum may be examined. Opening it carefully, the rudimentary sex organ can be plainly seen; with experience, one can be 100 per cent accurate.

INBREEDING

While inbreeding is not advisable, it is sometimes necessary to resort to it with rare species, where replacements cannot be obtained following losses. For about three generations there does not seem to be any obvious loss of vitality. There are instances of hundreds of pheasants in Europe and America, all descendants of a single imported pair. When dealing with large numbers such as this, it is best to pair the members most distantly related. There must be considerable inbreeding in the wild among game birds where new coverts have been laid down.

SEX CHANGING

It is a physiological fact that female birds in old age can change their plumage to resemble the male. In the pheasant, spurs are developed. All the male characteristics and colouring become noticeable. The same applies to the turkey, pea hen, domestic fowl, partridge, pigeon and wild duck. They stop laying eggs and they will not mate. The cause is atrophy of the female reproductive organs and development of the rudimentary male sex organs.

CHAPTER 8

PREDATORS: MAMMALS

When considering the destruction of predatory birds and animals a lot can be said for and against. In my opinion the rat, weasel, stoat and domestic cat gone wild are the only ones with no redeeming features, and these should be ruthlessly destroyed. Members of the crow family, magpie, sparrowhawk, greater and lesser blackbacked gull and the fox, while bad, should not be exterminated, although their numbers must be kept within limits.

Some creatures must be spared altogether since they are already on the point of extinction from shooting, poisoning, trapping and egg collectors. As vast forests have fallen to the woodsman's axe, their natural habitats have been destroyed and the gun, the cat and the rat have been introduced. Thousands of acres of bog have been drained and barren lands have been converted into food-producing soil; inevitably fur and feathered life disappears. Less and less undisturbed land is available for these creatures to live their lives in peace.

Cat

DOMESTIC CAT (*Felix domesticus*)

There are only two species of the Felidae, i.e. *Felix domesticus*, the domestic cat and *Felix catus*, the wild cat.

Nobody knows the origin of the cat or when it was domesticated. Some maintain that it sprang from the wild cat, although there are many factors against this theory. They have completely different body formation. In the wild cat the tail is of the same thickness throughout its length and carries a dark tuft of fur at its tip; the tail of the domestic cat tapers and carries no tuft at its end. The fur of the wild cat is thicker and its period of gestation is twelve days longer than that of the domestic. The fact that the grey domestic cat exhibits similar markings to the wild cat does not necessarily mean that it is closely related. The young lion carries similar stripes.

A natural instinct for hunting is bred in every cat and takes effect from an early age. A tiny kitten's fur will bristle at the smallest movement and it will start stalking almost from the time it can walk. The dear little purring pussy of the fireside, with its green inscrutable gaze, can become a gangster out of doors.

When domestic cats leave home permanently and take to the wild they can be really destructive. They then lead a solitary life; they hunt alone and will not tolerate another of their kind when doing so. They are fierce, cruel, subtle and artful; they catch their prey by surprise, never taking the trouble to hunt it down, and concealing their intentions until they are put into operation.

Cats will attack only animals and birds weaker than themselves. The female must hide her young or they will be eaten by the male. In the wild the kittens are produced in hollow trees, old rabbit burrows and holes.

After some generations in the wild state, domestic cats revert to the striped grey colouring of the wild cat and they grow much larger than their brethren at home. An appetite for pheasants in preference to rats or mice is impossible to cure. The domestic cat turned wild is most destructive and must be destroyed. However, one that must be forgiven is the blue-eyed male white cat, which is too conspicuous to be dangerous and is usually deaf. If they are albinos with red eyes, their sight is also defective.

One redeeming feature of the cat is the large number of rats and mice it destroys. In one respect a cat is unfortunate, if it kills a robin it is a murderer; if it kills a rat it is a hero—it must be difficult for a cat to know the difference.

WILD CAT (*Felix catus, Linn.*)

The wild cat is almost extinct in Europe, except in vast forests and inaccessible mountain ranges. Hybrids between the wild cat and domestic cat are said to have been obtained, although this is most unlikely. While the wild cat is most destructive to game it should be spared since it is so rare. Some large estate owners in Scotland actually protect them and do not deny them the few pheasants they take. In former days keepers and owners destroyed them out of hand.

Rat (*Mus decumanus*)

The first invader of the rat species was the small black rat. It came from the Levant and spread throughout the world on ships. It thrived until the larger brown rat arrived from Asia and quickly drove it to extinction. The brown rat is one of the greatest evils of all time. We are constantly reminded of their existence by their destructiveness and their powers of multiplication. No force can be effectively exerted against them, for nothing can stop their amazing propagation. Destroy them by the million and they seem to return with increased forces in a few weeks.

Figure 11. *Brown Rat*

The rat is omnivorous and it will go to the extent of eating its own comrades or young if hungry. One will destroy a whole nye of pheasant chicks in a very short time. It will take them one by one, kill them and store them to be eaten at its leisure.

My experience is that rats will not interfere with adult pheasants and that the pheasants do not seem to mind them. On one occasion my aviaries were suddenly infested by a swarm of rats—they burrowed underneath the wire from outside. One evening I was horrified to notice a dozen or so moving about among the birds and all getting along quite amiably; in fact a Golden cock was displaying to one. Traps were immediately laid in outside runs but they were too slow, catching only one or two each night. Intensive poisoning with a proprietary spread on buttered bread wiped them out in a short time. Their dead bodies were scattered all over the garden after two nights. If the pheasants had happened to be young, not one would have been left alive.

Rats will always travel under cover if at all possible. Their natural enemies are owls, cats, weasels, stoats and some hawks. They breed three times a year and have anything up to twelve young to each litter. Little good can be said for rats, but they do devour vast quantities of offal which would otherwise breed pestilence and flies.

Fox (Vulpes vulgaris)

Different species of fox are found all over the Northern Hemisphere. Their food consists of anything from lamb to beetles. The fox affords some benefit where packs of hounds are kept. Hunting gives employment and provides sport for a section of the community and in these areas the numbers of foxes will automatically be kept within limits. In other places they should be totally destroyed.

Figure 12. Fox

The fox is a crafty gangster. A skulk of foxes will travel several miles raiding farmyards for poultry. They can wreak terrible destruction in preserves where all sorts of game become their prey. They are a menace when young lambs are about, and have been even known to hunt for wild fowl and geese on the sea shore. A fox hunts by cunning, carefully reconnoitring first and then creeping up on his victims. If he cannot carry all his kills to earth he may bury them for a future meal. Since the shortage of rabbits the fox has been particularly troublesome.

Weasel Family

WEASEL (*Mustela vulgaris*)

The weasel is a fur-bearing animal. Its colouring is red above and white underneath. Its tail, 3 in. long, is red and of uniform thickness along its length. Its body is 7 in. long and 1½ in. high. This is a cruel, cunning, vicious little creature, which kills just for the sake of killing, and seems to gain enjoyment out of doing so. Weasels hunt in packs and will kill virtually anything; they will destroy a whole nye of young pheasants in a short time. Their method is to spring on a bird, kill it by one bite on the head, then go for another until all are dead. Nothing is safe up to the size of a hare. The more blood the more the weasel likes it, whether hungry or not. A weasel with teeth sunk in will cling to the neck of a rocketting pheasant until it drops to earth, dying from loss of blood.

Weasels hunt in an intelligent way—they are slow in pursuit so they conserve their strength while their prey is tiring. Eventually exhaustion and fear places it at their mercy. A rabbit becomes so terror-stricken that it stops and cries long before the weasel reaches it. The weasel will just lope along trailing its selected victim for miles, ignoring others it may meet on the way. It is amazing that, although a hare can race out of danger in a few seconds leaving a weasel far behind, it will just slowly hop along before its killer, lying down to await its fate as if hypnotised. Weasels have infinite patience: when it comes to hunting feeding pheasants, instead of trailing them the weasel will wait until the bird comes its way.

STOAT (*Mustela erminea*)

Stoats and weasels, apart from size and colour, have much in common. The stoat is 9 in. long. Its tail is tipped with black and is more bushy than that of the weasel. Its body is brown above and dusky white underneath. Its habits of killing are similar. In winter the stoat is ermine. It then sheds its brown coat and puts on a beautiful soft, light creamy white fur; the tip of the tail remains black. The fur produced in Europe is of very little commercial value. The finest ermine comes from Siberia.

PINE MARTEN (*Martes abietum*)

Among all the members of the weasel family this is the most agile and most formidable. Its colouring is very beautiful: brown with yellow throat and breast. It is 18 in. long, with a 10 in. tail. Since its skin is much in demand this animal is almost extinct. It was common in England 100 years ago. It will kill most things, including sheep, and can be very destructive to pheasants old and young. It gets its name from its habit of living in pine forests, where it climbs trees and silently moves about from branch to branch before coming suddenly on its victim. There may be a few specimens still in forests of North Europe and Asia.

COMMON, STONE, or BEECH MARTEN (*Martes Foine*)

This animal is more inclined to frequent farm buildings than the Pine Marten. Its colouring is brown, throat and breast are white. It is a notorious raider of poultry and pheasants. Nevertheless, since it is now exceedingly rare it should be protected from extinction.

Badger (*Melex taxus*)

The badger is now our only representative species of the Ursidae or bear family. It is our oldest quadruped. Fossil remains have been found to prove it existed with the great mammoths, the beaver and the elk, all of which have long since disappeared. In spite of persecution for millions of years, the badger has survived and still goes its own quiet way.

It is a model of tidiness. Everything offensive is removed from its sett and buried. The sett may cover up to half an acre of ground and consists of numerous tunnels and shelves, sleeping, eating and breeding quarters; a whole cete of badgers will occupy it. Nesting material, such as dry grass, bracken, leaves, etc., is collected in early autumn and when it is dry it is carried

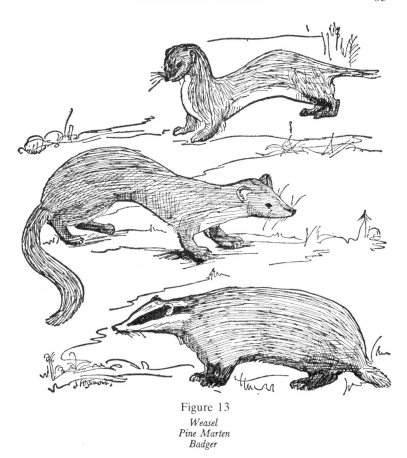

Figure 13
Weasel
Pine Marten
Badger

into the sett. It is carefully packed to make comfortable sleeping quarters.

The poor badger is subjected to cruel treatment—it is unjustly blamed for a lot of damage it does not do. The little harm done by it does not call for its wholesale persecution. It is not for nothing that persistently irritating a person is known as "badgering."

A badger will take eggs from a pheasant's nest if it comes across one accidentally on its nightly prowls. It will never find one by scent because nature has arranged that a sitting game bird has none. The badger is too slow to catch a pheasant unless it is sickly or wounded. Its favourite food consists of roots, fruit, berries, snails, worms, frogs, mice, beetles and honey with nest bees, wasps and all. Badgers become very tame and affectionate if caught and trained when young.

Hedgehog or Hedge Pig (*Erinaceus europaeus*)

Everybody is familiar with this harmless little animal. Its worst enemy is man, and boys think it fun to make a football of it. It is said that a fox will roll it into water and keep it there until it drowns. The only way apart from death that will make a hedgehog unroll is a wetting. If there is no pond available, the fox, knowing the animal's weakness, provides the necessary himself. The hedgehog is unjustly accused of many crimes which range from cow and goat sucking to raiding orchards and throwing down the fruit. In fact of course it does not suck cows or goats and it cannot climb trees. It has no means of attacking its enemies or defending itself by seeking flight: its only protection is its coat of sharp spines. It carries a species of flea peculiar to itself, Archaeopsylla Erinaci. If de-flead the animal will die.

Hedgehogs can become very tame and make great pets. If a house is infested with cockroaches or other noxious insects it will devour them all very quickly. They are easily fed on milk and kitchen scraps. A hedgehog will take pheasants' eggs and eat them in a most ingenious way: it lays the egg on the ground holding it with its fore-feet and then, after cutting an opening at the top of the egg with its teeth, it licks out the contents without spilling a drop. It will also take frogs, worms, beetles, roots, berries, fruit and various insects. Its habits are nocturnal and it remains in a torpid state of hibernation in an old rabbit burrow or hole in a tree stump throughout the winter.

Poachers

The greatest of all predators is the human poacher. In olden days professional poaching was an honourable calling. Poachers hunted with dogs, sticks, lamps and traps; modern weapons were unknown. The damage done was very little.

Sportsmen by nature—the culprits were good-natured rogues who matched their wits against keepers and owners. They had no close season and hunted night and day. If brought up in Court, they readily swore that they never killed a pheasant in their lives and were miles away from the preserve where the offence was supposed to have been committed.

The modern poacher is a different proposition. There are different types. Hundreds of them leave cities and towns in motor cars over week-ends and shoot indiscriminately, without the permission of the land owner. Another offender is the one who shoots with a rifle, telescopic site and silencer—he is no sportsman; he shoots for the market by creeping up on feeding pheasants. Another class of "sportsman" is the one who imagines that anything that is not game is an enemy and must be destroyed; he wants all for himself.

Another pest is the man who shoots everything. He keeps on killing to make a bag to be boasted of and then wonders when covering the same ground why game is scarce. A "sportsman" in America boasted of shooting 140,000 birds and animals in one year. Another shot 8000 wild geese. 1100 brace of wood-cock in one day with fifteen guns is a "proud" record. There is a monument in Scotland to a man who shot 40 grouse with one shot; having gorged themselves with corn, they were sitting on a wall and he got them in line. Punt gunners boasted of getting up to 500 duck with one shot.

When man arrived in these islands they were rich in bird and animal life, bear, wolf, beaver, eagle, auk and many others, all beautiful and free. That great ornithologist, Wilson of America, estimated that a passing flock of passenger pigeons in 1803 contained 200,000,000 birds. In 1914, the last specimen died in Chicago Zoo. They were all killed and their bodies were fed to pigs—the slaughter goes on.

Nature is having its revenge. Hitherto unknown armies of insects, grubs, parasites of all kinds and bacterial and virus diseases are attacking plant life. Destroy them with poison sprays and powders and they return in a new and more resistant form. Why? Because man has upset the balance of nature. Millions of birds and animals are killed every year by chemical poisons. Some species which not so many years ago were abundant are now almost extinct. In Southern Rhodesia, it is estimated that thirty million finches were killed in one season by poison sprays. In other areas bird life was completely wiped out by poisons. Birds eat millions of tons of harmful insects every year. Less birds means more insects; more insects means more poison sprays. Intensive spraying with insecticides in Africa is decimating our migratory species and the few that survive and reach our shores have to face the same treatment again. One can safely predict that in fifty or a hundred years bird life as we know it will have ceased to exist.

CHAPTER 9

PREDATORS: BIRDS

Golden Eagle (Chrysaetos)

This magnificent bird should be spared at all costs, since it is fast becoming extinct due to intensive poisoning, trapping and shooting. Although formerly very common in Ireland and Scotland, there are now very few breeding records. There are some in Scotland and one in Ireland in County Antrim (1957). No other bird has the strength of wing and poise of the Golden Eagle; it is able to soar, wheel, sail, mount, drop and hover—all without upsetting its grace of motion. It can climb beyond the field of human vision.

There is an old fable as to how the wren became the King of all birds. When a match was arranged among all the birds as to which would fly the highest, the wren tucked itself under the feathers of the eagle's wing. When the eagle easily went the highest the wren, fresh and full of vigour from its free ride, popped out and went up another few feet. The story does not relate how it returned to earth.

In olden days the wings and head of an eagle were portrayed as an emblem of strength, as are lions, dragons and bulls. The head should look to the right—looking to the left was a bad omen. America, Germany, Russia, Austria, Persia and Italy adopted it as a symbol of power. Different personages had different birds, depending on their rank, as symbols: an eagle for an Emperor; a gyrfalcon for a King; a peregrine for an Earl; a merlin for a Lady; a goshawk for a Squire and a sparrowhawk for a Clergyman.

The golden eagle has a wing-span of 7 ft to 8 ft in the male and 9 ft in the female. The wings are 24 in. wide and the body is 3 ft in length. It can climb at great speed and drop like a thunderbolt. The body is coloured reddish brown; the neck is golden red; the tail is light brown and grey; the legs are yellow and covered with feathers. Eagles pair for life and never separate except when the female is incubating. Even then the male only leaves the eyrie to obtain food for both.

The eyrie is built of sticks, bracken and grasses on a rocky summit beyond the reach of man. Two or three dusky white eggs, blotched with red, are laid.

In mountain valleys and fields eagles take a terrible toll of lambs and even battle with the deer. An eagle has been known to settle on the antlers of a stag and beat it about the face with its beak and wings until the poor animal, in a mad rush to rid itself of its tormentor, crashed down a cliff to its death. The eagle then enjoyed its meal in comfort.

Hawks and Falcons

PEREGRINE FALCON (*Falco peregrinus*)

This bird's back is bluish grey with dark bands; breast feathers are white, barred with brown; the beak is blue; the cere yellow; fcct are yellow; claws are black and the eggs are pale red spotted with deep red. The name falcon is now applied to birds of prey, of great courage and long wings, which take their victims as they move. As well as the peregrine, the merlin, hobby and kestrel are included. Peregrine means a wanderer. It is the most powerful for its size of all the birds of prey and is from 16 in. to 18 in. in length. The higher the victim soars to escape the more the peregrine seems to like it. It will kill for amusement, but will never take birds off the ground.

Travelling at over 200 miles an hour, according to an observation by an air pilot (though 150 m.p.h. would be a more usual figure), a tercil or male falcon in the stoop and then straightening out, will attack a team of duck in flight, a company of widgeon, a desert of lapwing, a spring of teal or a congregation of golden plover. With one blow of the wing to each bird when

Figure 14
Barn Owl
Golden Eagle
Sparrowhawk
Peregrine
Falcon   *Kestrel*

J. Fitzsimons

passing, as if just for practice, the falcon will kill several birds, which will drop to earth dead, the killer subsequently flying on without troubling to see what destruction it has caused. The peregrine's favourite prey is heron, and it will attack a sege of them returning to their tree-top nests. Many a falcon met its doom from a thrust of the heron's spear-like beak. It will take ravens and all sea-fowl including the greater blackbacked gull.

A peregrine's eyrie on cliff or mountain can be a protection to game birds. Gulls and crows will not come within miles of it and pheasants can rear their young in peace in the lowlands. The falcon is now rare in these islands. There is only one breeding record, i.e. in County Antrim (Ireland), 1958.

OSPREY (*Pandion haliaetus, Linn.*)

The colouring of this bird is somewhat similar to all the hawks. The head and neck feathers are white with brown streaks at the sides. The upper parts are dark brown. The underparts are white with yellow streaks. The tail is light brown with dark bands; the beak and cere are grey; the iris is yellow. Eggs are pale red and splashed with brown—three are laid in nests in cliffs or ruins.

The name is a corruption of ossifragus, the bonebreaker. Formerly fairly common in these islands, this bird is now rare although there may still be specimens in Scotland. The osprey lives mostly on fish which it neatly picks out of the water, gripped by both claws in the centre of the body. The fish is carried with the head pointing in the direction of flight to lessen wind resistance.

SPARROWHAWK (*Accipiter nisus, Linn.*)

A white spot on the nape of the neck and long yellow legs make this bird distinctive in the hawk family. Today this is probably our commonest bird of prey. The word hawk means a seizer—a seizer of sparrows. When the sparrowhawk appears it strikes abject terror into the bird population; all song is suspended, and birds become frozen to their perches; not a sound is to be heard. By this time the selected victim is quickly snatched up and carried away to be eaten in some sheltered spot.

The sparrowhawk seems to have no redeeming feature. Its

broad powerful tail renders it capable of performing the most astonishing evolutions with ease. It can do immense damage to pheasants, when it dashes in, strikes and is gone in a flash with a bird. The gun is the only answer. Where young birds are being reared it must be at the ready all the daylight hours.

The sparrowhawk has a world-wide distribution. The male, 12 in. long, is smaller than the female, which is 15 in. long, including the tail. The male is often confused with the smaller harmless hawks. It will kill on the wing, on the ground or in trees, and will dash through dense thickets, hedges or even glass, without pausing in pursuit of its victim. It can take a woodquest, three times its weight, in mid-air.

In the breeding season the nest can be discovered by a mass of feathers, casts and droppings under a tree. The eggs are light blue streaked with brown. It can be shot out in the same way as the magpie and hooded crow.

COMMON or HEN HARRIER (*Cirus cyaneus, Linn.*)

In this bird the tail is longer than the wings; upper parts of the body are grey; lower parts are whitish; the beak is black. This hawk is related to the owls inasmuch as the eyes and face are similar, their feathers are also soft and downy and they fly silently. The bird gets its name from its manner of harrying its prey. It ranges slowly near the ground like a hunting dog. When a victim is spotted, it soars to about 30 ft, pauses to get its sight and then drops to strike its victim dead with one blow. It is becoming very rare and should not be destroyed. It nests in high heather.

MARSH HARRIER (*Cirus aeruginosus, Linn.*)

The back is reddish brown; tail is grey; breast, head and neck are very pale yellow; lower parts are rusty; beak is black and feet are yellow. Formerly fairly common in Ireland, this bird is now very rare, and should be protected before it becomes extinct. Its habits are the same as those of the common harrier. It preys on small rats, mice, frogs, slugs, beetles, etc. It nests on level ground in long grass. Four white eggs are laid.

MONTAGUE HARRIER (*Cirus cineraceus montague*)

In this bird the wings are longer than the tail. The upper

plumage is blue grey; the underparts are white, streaked with orange; the beak is black. It was first described by a Colonel Montague. The hawk is noted for its long wings, enabling it to stay for long periods in flight. Its habits and food are similar to the other harriers. It nests on the ground without any cover. Its eggs are light blue with brownish spots.

GYRFALCON (*Falco caudicans, Linn.*)

The plumage of the gyrfalcon is mainly white with dark spots and streaks. The tail is longer than the wings; the beak is blue; cere and feet are yellow. The name is probably derived from the low latin Gyrofalco. The bird is also known as the Gerfalcon or Iceland Falcon. It is the most magnificent of the family. Although formerly common in Northern parts of both hemispheres, it is now almost extinct. It is a bold marauder and it will even attack a skein of geese in flight. Its food consists of pheasants and other game birds, rabbits, hares and seafowl. The gyrfalcon may still be found in the mountains of Scandinavia, where it makes its nest of sticks and seaweed. Three eggs are laid.

KESTREL (*Falco tinnunculus, Linn.*)

The plumage of this bird is grey in the back, neck and breast; underparts are yellowish red; beak is blue; feet and cere are yellow. Kestrel is a true falcon, as seen from the length of its wings and shape of its beak. Also known as Windhover, Stemgale, Stanel Hawk and Creshawk, the kestrel can be recognised by its way of staying still in the air as if riding on an air current. Having surveyed an area of ground it moves on a few feet and again hovers, staying in the air without any apparent wing movement. When it spots something moving in the grass it folds its wings and drops to earth like a flash.

Its food is mainly mice, rats, frogs, beetles, grasshoppers, earthworms and it often takes flying insects in the air, picking them off with one claw and eating them. It is often mistaken for a sparrowhawk, unfortunately, for it will do no harm to pheasants. The kestrel nests in cliffs, ruins, high trees and church towers. Eggs are white with dark red blotches.

HOBBY (*Falco subutteo, Linn.*)

In this bird the tail is longer than the wings. The bird's back is bluish black; underparts are reddish yellow marked with brown; beak is blue; cere and feet are yellow. This is another windhover like the Kestrel and its habits and food are the same. Skylarks are commonly taken and dung beetles are a dainty. It nests in high trees. Four creamy white eggs splashed with red are laid.

MERLIN or STONE FALCON (*Falco aesolan, Linn.*)

The back of this bird is pale greyish blue; the underparts are yellow with brown streaks; the tail, longer than the wings, is black and barred; the beak is blue; cere and feet are yellow. This is our smallest hawk. Although no bigger than a thrush, it is afraid of nothing, and will attack birds several times its own size. Its main food consists of blackbirds, thrushes, finches, mice and frogs. It has been known to take pheasant chicks. The Merlin nests in heather. Four eggs, light brown with reddish brown blotches are laid.

GOSHAWK or GOOSEHAWK (*Astur palumbarius, Linn.*)

The plumage is blue grey above and underparts are white, streaked with brown; tail, brown and barred has a white tip; beak is blue; legs are yellow. The goshawk or goosehawk, is very rare in these islands. It is one of the largest hawks, the male being 20 in. in length with 12 in. wing, and the female 23 in. long, with 14 in. wings. In parts of Europe where it is not uncommon, it is very destructive to pheasants of all ages. It nests in high trees. Four white eggs splashed with brown are laid.

BUZZARD (*Buteo vulgaris*)

The upper parts, head and neck of this bird are dark brown; the lower parts are light brown streaked with darker brown; the beak is grey; cere and legs are yellow. The word buzzard is derived from the Latin *Butes*, used for a large number of birds of prey, including the common buzzard and the harriers. It has a world-wide distribution with the exception of Australia. Formerly common in Ireland and Scotland, it is now becoming very rare, but it is becoming more common in southern England.

It is a sluggish bird and can only catch its prey by an element of surprise. It hunts noiselessly, ranging slowly over the ground and pouncing before its victim can think of escaping. It will take young pheasants, small birds, frogs, mice, rats and it will feed on carrion. It will seek the latter when soaring and wheeling high in the clouds in circles. It descends gradually and then ranges, all the time keeping an eye on the site of its prey. It nests in cliffs or high trees. Four white eggs with greenish spots are laid.

KITE (*Milvus ictinus*)

The upper parts are brown; head and neck are grey with brown streaks; underparts are reddish brown; the feet are yellow. Now very rare, this hawk was once the most familiar bird of prey in these islands, being commonly seen in the streets of large cities, where it lived on garbage. Few know that the paper kite flown by children was named from the bird that floated all day over the heads of the inhabitants. When the systematic destruction of all hawks by gamekeepers began it almost disappeared. Although it may be a rare winter visitor in Ireland, there is no record of it and it is believed extinct here.

The Kite is recognised by its sword-like wings, 5 ft span, long forked tail and easy flight. It has a gliding imperceptible movement and rarely flaps its wings. It will take small birds, rats, mice, young rabbits, young pheasants, partridge, grouse and fish. The nest, built in high trees, is constructed of sticks, grass, rags, old rope, paper, in fact any loose waste. The eggs, two to four in number, are white with red and brown markings.

Owls

There are twenty-nine species of owls distributed over the world. Of seven found in these islands some are only casual visitors and there are only three commonly resident.

Owls have striking characteristics, all bearing a relation to their nocturnal mode of living. The plumage is soft and silky, rendering their flight noiseless. Their eyes are large with immense pupils, so that every ray of light is availed of when they come out to feed. The eyes are placed looking directly forward, differing from the hawks and eagles, where the eyes are at the side of the head.

Owls are blind in bright light. The large ear holes are covered by a flap or lid which they can open and shut at will. Owing to their wings being short and round they do not possess the same powers of flight as the hawks. Their legs are powerful and furnished with sharp claws; one toe of each foot is reversible as in the parrot family. Any little harm owls do is more than repaid by the enormous number of rats and mice they destroy.

BARN or SCREECH OWL (*Strix flammea, Linn.*)

Nowadays this is the owl most commonly found in these islands and it is generally distributed all over Europe, Asia and Africa. The colour is reddish brown, mottled with grey and small black and white spots; underparts are white; the legs are brown; the eyes are black.

The barn owl likes to stay close to farms and human habitations, where its food is abundant. The bird sleeps in a barn, church tower or hollow tree and cannot get a day's rest without hiding, for if it sits outside, it is mobbed all day by other birds and cannot even see its tormentors.

When the sun goes down the barn owl is lord of its territory; it is now a different character. It skims in and out of barns, haggards and hedgerows in a systematic search, wreaking destruction on the little creatures who venture forth for food and play under the cover of darkness. It will take young rabbits, rats, mice, frogs, small birds, moths, beetles and even fish, which are taken from the top of the water by a quick snatch with the claws of one leg. Mice are the main food and they are sometimes swallowed alive. After seizing its prey it screeches when carrying it off—hence the name screech owl.

When rearing young the barn owl will take a mouse or young rat every ten to fifteen minutes. On this account it must be forgiven for any depredations it does to young pheasant chicks, which are counterbalanced by the amount of good it does in destroying predators. Several broods of young are reared every year, a second laying taking place before the first brood leaves the nest. The nest is usually made in a hollow tree and four to five white eggs are laid.

BROWN or TAWNY OWL (*Surnium aluco, Linn.*)

The colouring of this bird is mainly brown, marked with

black, grey and dark brown spots; underparts are reddish with brown bars; the legs are feathered to the claws.

This is the only owl that hoots, as Shakespeare wrote,

"Then nightly sings the staring owl tu-whit;
  to-who, a merry note."

With the exception of the barn owl, it is the commonest species in Northern Europe and in our own islands. It is a small owl, being only fifteen inches in length. It is supposed to be a bird of evil omen. Its food consists of small animals, birds and insects; it will take young pheasants only if they wander after sunset, which is very unlikely. It is an expert fisherman: it sits on a stone in the middle of a river and when a fish comes to the surface near enough it is picked up by a quick movement of a foot. When rearing young it becomes savage and will attack humans as well as dogs or cats. The nest is made in a hollow tree and is formed from bones, fur and other remains of its victims.

SNOWY OWL (*Nyctea scandiaca, Linn.*)

The adult is pure white with a light russet brown tail and underparts; the beak is black and the legs are clothed in white feathers; the claws are black. Large orange eyeballs set in white plumage give the bird a strikingly beautiful appearance. There is no breeding record in these islands. It is a winter visitor.

As well as being nocturnal this owl is also diurnal, the eyes and ears not being so highly developed as in the purely nocturnal species. Since they are most commonly found close to the Arctic Circle, nocturnal habits would be of little use if they were unable to hunt in bright light, for there is little darkness in those latitudes in summer.

The snowy owl is distributed over the northern parts of both hemipheres. It will kill on the wing like a falcon, and take chick, pheasant, grouse, pigeon and other birds. It will also take fish, picking them off the water neatly with one foot when in flight.

All the snowy owls of Scandinavia, or for that matter of Europe, gather for the lemming migration which takes place about every twenty years. For the feast, with the owls, also come all the hawks and all the other birds and beasts of prey, although there appear to be more snowy owls than any other because their colouring makes them more conspicuous. The hawks circle the sky. All wait. The fast-multiplying little brown and black furred, vole-like rodents, finding their mountain-top homes overcrowded and foodless, start their journey into the west. By instinct they are said to seek the lost continent of Atlantis, where their ancestors went in search of food in time of famine.

In teeming millions they come, feeding on reindeer moss and plants. No obstacle stops them, mountains, cliffs, rivers, swamps, villages or towns. When crossing a river so many thousands drown that the others cross on a raft made of the dead bodies. On they go until they reach the sea and there they stop. They become so tightly packed that one moves in and starts to swim, then another and another and finally, the whole mass takes to the water and swims to—they do not know where. They never reach their El Dorado, but drown in their millions. It is all over. Not a lemming is to be seen again until the next migration. All the owls and the hawks and the beasts and birds of prey leave, disconsolate, but well fed. The feast is finished.

LONG EARED OWL (*Otus vulgaris*)

Its name derived from its long, dark brown feathers or "ears" growing in tufts from its head, this bird has a large geographical range and is common in our islands. According to Ussher and Warren, in 1900, it was our commonest species of owl and breeds in every country of the British Isles. It is purely nocturnal and never hunts in daylight. Since it lives in deep plantations it is rarely seen. Its body colour is brown with dark streaks all over. It adopts the nest of any large bird in a tree such as crow, magpie, or heron, or nests in a hollow. Its food is similar to that of the other owls but it will take well-grown pheasant chicks. It does not do much harm and should be spared since it takes enormous numbers of mice and rats.

SHORT EARED OWL (*Otus brachyotus*)

The upper plumage of this bird is dark brown with yellow markings; underparts are orange red, streaked with brown. Otherwise known as the mouse hawk, honed ooulent, or hawk owl, this is a winter visitor in Ireland. It has never bred here.

Figure 15. *Long-eared Owl*

It nests in marshes in long sedge or rushes and is well hidden by overhanging herbage. The short-eared owl will take birds much larger than itself and is a fearless little hunter.

Magpie (*Pica caudata, Linn.*)

The correct name of this rascal is the pie from its pied plumage. The prefix is the abbreviation of Margaret. Other birds with such prefixes are Jenny Wren; Peggy Whitethroat; Dick Dunnock (the hedge sparrow); Charlie Wheatear; King Harry (goldfinch); Jack Daw; Jinny owl; Billybiter (bluetit); Bessy dooker (dipper); Willywicket (Sandpiper) and Robin, which is an abbreviation of Robert. Other names for magpie are piot, madge, mag, maggie, pianet, hagister.

What a pity that this beautiful bird in its metallic green, blue, bronze and white must be placed with the top scoundrels. Its choice food is young birds and eggs, and it can do much damage to young pheasants in the rearing field. The magpie feeds well in times of hard frost and snow, killing small birds and animals already dying of hunger. The magpie is easily destroyed by poisons and shooting, but it should not be exterminated, since our bird life is gradually being decimated and it is one of our most beautiful feathered creatures.

The magpie nests usually in a thorn bush. The whole nest is surrounded with thorny brambles and an opening just sufficient to admit the bird is left at the side. Five or six light blue eggs with small dark spots are laid.

Jay *(Garrulus glandarius, Linn.)*

This beautiful bird is much maligned. It is dressed in cobalt blue, metallic black, turquoise and cinnamon. The tail is white. The brilliant colouring makes it conspicuous when flashing through the forest. Jays will not take pheasants' eggs—they prefer those of small birds. Their main food consists of young birds, including pheasant chicks, also insects, moths, beetles, fruit berries, nuts and acorns.

They do good when their warning cry, which is a harsh scream, resounds throughout the forest, when a more notorious gangster appears, setting every living thing on the alert. It is a signal that a murderer is at large and other birds get a chance to look after their own safety. Jays are great planters of acorn and beechmast; they bury the seeds singly all over the open spaces in the forests, taking them from under trees where they could not grow for want of sunshine. In this way they assist afforestation. They feed their young by regurgitated food like a pigeon. They really do very little harm and as they do add to the pleasures of our countryside they must be spared. The nest of sticks, grass and moss, is built in a tree and five eggs are laid.

Crow Family

Raven *(Corvus corax)*

The plumage of the raven is black with a purple sheen. The nest is a mass of sticks placed on a cliff ledge. Six green eggs with brown spots are laid.

The raven is the largest member of the crow family; it is 20 in. in length. It is distributed all over the earth even into the Arctic Circle and inhabits the wildest regions, mountains, sea cliffs and forests. It rarely approaches civilisation. It will eat anything dead or alive, fish, animal or vegetable, fresh or rotting. With an injured or dying animal it starts by picking out the most dainty morsel, the eyes. The unfortunate victim

is then at its mercy and with powerful strokes of its sharp beak it is quickly killed. This frequently happens with sheep. It will not usually take pheasants but sometimes one turned rogue will raid poultry and game runs.

The raven is held to be a bird of evil omen. There are all sorts of fables attached to it; they forecast the future and will desert their haunts before a catastrophe strikes; they contain the souls of the damned; witches ride on their backs; he who hears a raven laugh will die shortly.

The raven is one of the oldest birds in written history. The first bird specifically mentioned in the Bible was the raven. Noah sent a raven forth from the Ark to bring back tidings of the fall of the waters. In doing this he knew that the raven was more clever than the others. He knew it would return. When the Almighty wanted a feathered servant to do His will, he chose the raven. Our Lord said in the New Testament "consider the ravens; that they sow not, neither reap; which have no store, chamber or barn; and God feedeth them. How much more value are ye than the birds?"

The raven pairs for life. Tamed it can be very gentle, and is a great linguist when trained; in this respect it is even better than the parrot. Ravens live up to eighty years.

CARRION CROW (*Corvus corone, Linn.*)

In spite of the constant persecution over the years, this bird is still with us but not now in such numbers as formerly. In some parts of these islands it is exceedingly rare. The scaul crow seems to have banished it. It is beautifully coloured in glossy black, tinged with purple and green. The head and neck are tinged with green. It nests in high trees beyond the reach of man. Six green eggs splashed with olive brown are laid.

Carrion crows pair for life. They can be distinguished from others of the crow family by their heavy, laboured flight. They are omnivorous, living on carrion, eggs, fish, rats, mice, young

---

Figure 16

Carrion Crow

Tawny Owl   *Osprey*

Jay   *Goshawk*

birds, insects, grain or fruit. They can do a lot of damage to pheasants by taking their eggs and chicks.

While all the members of the crow family are harmful to pheasants they are also scavengers, devouring masses of decaying animal and vegetable matter; in this way they do some good.

HOODED CROW (*Corvus Cornix, Linn.*)

The wings, head and tail of this bird are black. The remainder of the body is ash grey. The female is smaller than the male and the grey plumage is tinged with brown. Many years ago a casual visitor in these islands, it has now come to stay with a vengeance. It is known by many names: Rogston; Scaul; Grey Saddleback; Dun Crow; Kentish Crow; Norway Crow and Greyback.

These crows are now widespread and becoming more plentiful yearly. The nest in a tree is solitary. Five greenish eggs with light brown spots are laid. When the female is discovered to be sitting the male can be shot first, then nest and female can be shot out.

Poisoning is the quickest method of destroying all members of the crow family, but it is dangerous to lay poison in their haunts except in the following manner. If the carcass of a dead animal such as a sheep or calf can be obtained, it should be deposited on an island in a lake or river and liberally poisoned with strychnine or phosphorus. Hundreds of crows, gulls and magpies will be destroyed and the surrounding countryside will be safe for eggs and young birds for that season. A poisoned animal can be left in the centre of a ploughed field but it must be watched and picked up when not under observation.

The hoodie is prince of predators. When food is scarce it will search the seashore for ailing sea birds, crabs, worms, dead fish, in fact anything. It will carry shell fish to a height and drop them to break the shell. In the breeding season hoodies

---

Figure 17

Hooded Crow
            Jackdaw
         Hen Harrier
Magpie   *Common*
           Gull

effect immense destruction. They turn to eggs and young birds for food. They range moors, hedges, woods and dales in search of food all day. At this time poisoned eggs are successful or an egg laid beside a trap. A flesh bait can also be laid beside a trap—never allow it to become maggoty or you will surely catch a pheasant.

Gulls

GREATER BLACKBACKED GULL (*Larus marinus, Linn.*)

The head of this bird is pure white; the bill is yellow; the lower mandible is splashed with orange; the eyelids are yellow; the back is dark grey; tail and tail coverts are white; the legs are flesh coloured.

The Greater Blackbacked Gull belongs to a group of sea birds of the Genus Larus. Of fifty-two species of gulls, the most dangerous predators are the Greater and Lesser Blackbacked. They do most damage in the early spring, before they go to their nesting quarters. They then come inland to follow the plough, picking up game and poultry chicks as a change from worms. They seek their food by the seashore or in estuaries and only in very stormy weather will they come inland. Their appetites are omnivorous, they will eat anything dead or alive. The Greater Blackbacked has been known to swallow a half grown pheasant, rabbit, grouse and partridge. I saw one take a wounded mallard off a river. Every time the bird was attacked it dived and when it came up again the gull was waiting; it was in no hurry. Eventually the mallard gave up the struggle and the gull just picked it up in its beak and flew away. Gulls have been known to swallow a live kitten, and will readily slaughter a lamb; like the raven they start by picking out the eyes. Since they usually travel singly or in pairs they are easily shot or poisoned. They nest in marshes. Three large olive eggs spotted with brown are laid.

LESSER BLACKBACKED GULL (*Larus fuscus, Linn.*)

The head and neck of this bird are white in summer and in the winter they are streaked with brown; the back is dark grey; the bill, iris and feet are yellow; the underparts are white. It is distributed almost all over the world. It is another anarchist but not quite so bad as its big brother. Nevertheless, it can do a lot of damage to young pheasants.

The bird nests in cliffs or lake islands. The eggs are light brown in colour with darker brown spots.

Figure 18   SIAMESE FIREBACK PHEASANTS
(*Euplocamus prelatus*).

Figure 19   REEVES' PHEASANTS
(*Phasianus Reevesii*).

CHAPTER 10

ACTION AGAINST PREDATORS

Identification of the Culprit

This is a very interesting study gained from experience. One can tell fairly accurately from the condition of the remains of the victim and the place where it is found what caused its death. If the victim is a pigeon, woodquest or pheasant, found partly eaten under a tree, then the killer is a sparrowhawk. If the remains of several young pheasants are found huddled in a hidden corner of a field or yard and eaten from the back, between the wings and towards the head, the culprit is a rat. He will always leave the whole head and bones. A cat will devour its kill anywhere. It will also start to eat the back between the wings, leaving only the skin, large bones and beak. It will not bury the remains of its meal.

A fox will eat the head first and when satisfied, he will bury the surplus. You will also notice the saliva from the fox's mouth adhering to the mauled carcass. A fox will not return to his kill if he can get a fresh one unless he is hungry. A magpie, crow, raven or gull will always start by picking out the eyes of any bird or animal large or small, dead or alive, before proceeding to eat. A weasel or stoat will usually only eat a portion from the back of the neck.

Lure

If a rearing field is frequented by magpies or members of the crow family, a lure, in the form of a stuffed cat or fox, partly hidden in long grass or in the branch of a tree, will provide good shooting when they gather around to mob the dummy. The latest lure is a tape or wire recording of the distress call of a bird or small animal, set off automatically at intervals.

Traps

Traps, although cruel, must at times be the only solution. The steel trap is the usual one in use. Animals have a keen sense of smell so a new trap should be buried for a few days to pick up the earthy odour. They should be in good order and sensitive to snapping. The joints should be well oiled. Cage traps which catch the predators alive are now on the market and can be supplied by game requisite dealers, or they can be knocked up quite cheaply at home. Trapping is an art which can only be perfected by experience and by a study of the habits of preying animals. Camouflage must suit the surroundings. Do not cover a trap with sand or earth where there is none, or with grass where there is sand or earth.

The chain and peg must be well secured and covered with the same material as that covering the traps. A baited trap works well for the taking of scaul, crow or magpie. Any small animal partly skinned should be used. Traps are useful when there is snow about. They can be left directly in the run for rats or weasels. Stepping stones can be arranged over a shallow stream and left for a few days, then removed from the centre and a trap put down instead with the pan just at water level. Pole traps are illegal and kill more innocent than harmful birds.

Tunnel trapping is very successful for rats, weasels or stoats and it can be arranged so that domestic birds or animals do not get hurt. A tunnel may be made from old boards, slates, stones or piping laid along a fence or tree trunk. Leave it for a while before setting the traps so that the culprits may become familiar with it. A baited trap is not necessary but soil formation is important. The trap must be covered to harmonise with the surroundings; anything unusual will arouse suspicion. If rats are coming from an old drain or shore, an earthenware pipe leading from there to the pheasant run will always be availed of for cover. Steel traps for the fox are not effective. If too sharp it will take off the animal's paw and if too blunt he will pull his foot through it. In either case pain is caused without killing the fox and this must be avoided for the animal cannot help his nature.

Trapping weasels can be very successful, since they are continually on the move through walls, fences, hedges and up and down trees; they can drag their little bodies through the tiniest opening. Traps should be set over a wide area. There is nothing better than a drop of a dead female weasel's urine on the pan of the trap—this never fails to attract all those in the vicinity; a weasel carcass is also a good bait.

Shooting is the most certain method of destroying this predator. When the alarm call is given by any wild bird that the enemy is at large, it is only necessary to be on the alert, stay perfectly still and look where mobbing is going on and if the weasel is running, curiosity will make him stop to look— curiosity has cost many a weasel its life. When trailing his prey a weasel is an easy shot. He is concerned with and his mind is concentrated on one thing only and that is a spot under the victim's ear, where lies the jugular vein. If he is frightened away from a kill and is still hungry he will return immediately. A bitch out with her litter of up to ten kittens marching in single file can be easily wiped out with a gun.

Poisons

For rats many proprietary poisons are on the market and they are very successful, but they must be laid down regularly and not wait until a bad infestation occurs. The poisons may be thrust down holes in hedges, yards and houses. While poisoned eggs are useful, one must be careful as to where they are placed. The egg should be partly blown and the poison inserted with a syringe. Pieces of calcium carbide, dropped into holes which are then sealed off, will evict the tenants by another route and terriers can do the rest.

I find the best way is to lay the poison in old earthenware or concrete pipes where the rats run.

Poison gas is the easiest and most effective way of destroying the fox. A whole district can be quickly cleared by cyanide gas pumped into the earths which are then stopped. In the breeding season whole litters can be wiped out. Cyanide causes paralysis of the nervous system, death is instantaneous and there is no suffering. A poisoned dead cat (choice fox food) or an old hen half buried is deadly. A fox will eat a dead rat, a dog will not, so here again the bait can safely be poisoned. Bait should not be touched by the human hand unless unavoidable.

Figure 20 PEACOCK PHEASANTS
(*Polyplectron chinquis*).

CHAPTER 11

DISEASES, INJURIES AND PARASITES

Diseases

Pheasants are generally healthy birds, much more so than domestic poultry. Most illness belongs to one of two types—nutritional or infectious.

NUTRITIONAL DISEASES

With modern methods of feeding nutritional diseases are not common. In the wild, since pheasants have such a vast variety of food they never occur. With penned birds the nutritional diseases which concern us mostly are:

Rickets which is due to a deficiency of Vitamin D. It can occur at any age until the chick is four months old. Symptoms are spreading of the legs, the bones are thickened and the skull is flattened and depressed.

Curling Toes, which was once thought to be due to a weakness of the chick when hatched, or sudden change in the egg temperature some hours before hatching or inbreeding, is now known to be a Vitamin B deficiency.

Roup is a respiratory disease. It is recognised by a sticky, yellowish substance discharging from the nostrils, eyes and mouth. It is due to lack of Vitamin A.

Six Day Chick Disease. This disease is due to wrong feeding. There is a general absence of vitamins and chicks die when a week old.

Perosis. In Perosis the leg joints become enlarged and the leg bones are twisted. It is due to an excess of phosphates; manganese will cure it.

PROTOZOAN DISEASES

Protozoan diseases are fatal if not properly treated.

Coccidiosis is the commonest. The organisms of this disease remain in the intestine of apparently healthy birds and are evacuated in the bird's motions and so go on to infect others. Pheasants have their own order, i.e. *Eimeria pasiani*. A heavy infestation among chicks can be very serious and can wipe out the whole stock in a few days.

Symptoms—bird becomes fluffed; eyes shut up; and there is blood in the droppings. It can be kept under control by any of the sulpha group of drugs. Premises should be thoroughly cleaned and disinfected.

Blackhead or *Histomoniasis*. This is another disease of the Protozoan group. The organism can live in the ground for several years. Many domesticated birds are carriers of the organism without showing any symptoms of the disease itself. It is recognised by the greenish yellow liquid droppings and drooping head, wings and tail. Commercial preparations now on the market will cure it if taken in time—if in an advanced state it will end fatally.

FUNGUS DISEASES

The worst offender in this group is Aspergillosis. Birds become infected by *Aspergillus fumigatus*. It can become widespread in sleeping quarters which are damp and not kept clean. The mould can be seen growing everywhere on perches and walls. The spores are inhaled by the birds and the resulting mould blocks up the trachea or windpipe and lungs. The condition is incurable if allowed to go too far. If caught early a preparation of Streptomycin will cure it. About five drops of tincture of iodine in an ounce of drinking water is effective. All indoor and outdoor quarters and perches should be thoroughly limewashed. To the lime a non-poisonous disinfectant should be added.

BACTERIAL DISEASES

Pulloram or *Bacillary White Diarrhoea* (*B.W.D.*) is the commonest disease under this heading. It is recognised by continuous white liquid droppings. The organism is carried from an infected female through the egg to the chick. The only way to prevent it on a game farm is to put down blood tested stock.

Treatment is not very successful. Chicks so young are not resistant to disease and they are overcome too quickly for treatment to be of any use. Antibiotics can be tried in the drinking water or given by a pipette if the bird is too ill to drink.

Psittacosis. This disease is so-called because the causal organism, *Bacillus psittacosis*, was formerly only isolated from the psittacine family of parrot-like birds.

It is now known that many other birds become infected and remain carriers, i.e. fulmars, canaries, finches, domestic poultry, pheasants, pigeons and doves, especially the latter. The condition can only be diagnosed in a laboratory. Modern antibiotics will cure it.

Fowl Typhoid and *Paratyphoid.* Fowl typhoid will attack pheasants of any age and can kill off the whole stock in a few days. It can only be accurately diagnosed in the laboratory. It can be cured by the antibiotic drugs. Once again, it is better to prevent it by having blood tested stock only.

Erysipelas. All birds can be affected by *Erysipelothrix rhusiopathiae.* It also is responsible for the disease in pigs. It is highly infectious. The bird's wings, head and tail droop; droppings are liquid greenish yellow. Affected birds should be destroyed and their bodies burned.

Fowl Cholera. In this disease the bird's head becomes swollen; breathing is forced; the droppings are liquid. Fowl cholera will attack young or old stock. The disease is rapid and fatal, birds dying a few hours after showing signs of illness. Nothing can be done for it.

Avian Tuberculosis is invariably fatal, the victim simply wasting away. If in doubt as to the diagnosis an expert should be consulted. If several birds of the same stock are seen to be infected the only thing to do is to destroy the lot. Burn or deeply bury the carcasses in lime, thoroughly disinfect all the pens and start again with fresh stock.

Navel Ill. This is caused by bacteria entering through the navel of a newly hatched chick; they die before reaching a week old. It is one of the chief causes of whole clutches of chicks being wiped out in a few days after hatching. Touching the unhealed umbilical cord with tincture of iodine may help to kill the bacteria before they enter the body.

Botulism or *Timberneck.* It is also known as western duck sickness. This disease is due to poisoning by a toxin produced from decomposed food. Birds become weak in the legs and head and wings droop; there is often twisting of the neck and convulsions. As this weak condition is also common to other complaints, botulism may be difficult to diagnose without laboratory tests. There is no cure, but if the bird is strong it may be able to overcome it.

VIRUS DISEASES

Air Sac Disease can be very common and can have fatal results. I lost a number of half-grown pheasants from it. I noticed an air-swelling in the neck of quite healthy birds and knowing nothing about the condition, I gave the sac a nip from a sharp scissors where the skin was ballooned out, releasing the air. Although at the time all seemed well, overnight the sac filled with air again and the birds were found dead in the morning; the swelling had pressed on the windpipe and choked the birds. I found that by giving a liquid antibiotic in the drinking water, or a powdered one in the food, the disease was cured quickly.

Newcastle Disease or *Fowl Pest.* This is a virus disease which gets its name from the fact that the first major outbreak occurred many years ago in Newcastle on Tyne. The symptoms are running nostrils and eyes and green liquid droppings; the bird's neck is twisted and it keeps looking up to the sky. There is no cure.

Fowl Plague is a very rare disease in Northern Europe.

Fowl Pox. Nodules appear on comb, wattles and skin. Infected birds must be destroyed.

PARASITIC DISEASES

Gapes. I found that by far the greatest killer of chicks is the Gapeworm, *Syngamus trachea.* As well as pheasants it attacks domestic chicks, ducks, geese, turkeys, blackbirds, thrushes, starlings, magpie, crow, rook, partridge, grouse and a great many other varieties of birds. It kills only young birds; adults, while commonly infected, are strong enough to cough up the offender. In waterfowl the causative parasite is different from that of land birds.

The earthworm is the intermediate host. When the earthworm is eaten by a chick the gapeworm embryo is liberated and makes its way through the lymphatic system to the lungs, where it passes through the nymph stage and acquires sexual maturity. It then makes its way to the trachea or windpipe and uniting with another of its kind they attach themselves by suckers and by blocking up the pipe they obstruct the breathing. The first warning one gets is hearing a bird coughing. It becomes very distressed and gapes for breath; at the same time it tries to cough up the obstruction. It goes off its food, its wings droop and if not relieved in a short time it dies from hunger, suffocation and exhaustion.

The time from swallowing the worm to the embryo reaching the trachea is seven days and in another week the eggs, now laid in the windpipe, are mature enough to be coughed up and so are again swallowed by birds and passed in the excreta. They hatch out in the soil, enter the earthworm and start the cycle again. Warm, wet weather is favourable; in dry weather the earthworm cannot come to the surface of the soil. A few minutes of bright sunshine will render the larvae harmless.

To avoid the trouble, chicks should not be reared on ground that has been previously used for rearing poultry or pheasants for at least three years, or on wet low-lying soil. All rearing grounds should have a good dressing of lime some weeks before chicks are released. Bodies of victims which died should be buried, for the larvae will live even although the carcass of the host is decomposed.

Inhalant powders tend to kill more birds than they cure. A dessertspoonful of solution of 10 per cent salicylate of soda, added to a saucerful of drinking water, is very good. Garlic will kill the larvae in the bowel. Dipping the chick's beak in paraffin can be successful.

When a bird is badly infested and cannot breathe, the following method will not fail. Hold the chick in the left hand, keeping the legs held firmly between the fourth and little fingers and the head between the first finger and thumb, at the same time with the same fingers, keep the beak open. An assistant should then grip the tongue firmly with a forceps and pull it out. Dip the tip of a small stiff feather or looped horse hair in turpentine and plunge it down the opening into the windpipe which can easily be seen; twist the feather as you go in and keep twisting it as you withdraw it; the worm, red in colour and about $\frac{1}{3}$ in. in length, comes away and the bird gets instant relief. Other cures are to inject into the windpipe one drop of a mixture of half a teaspoonful of terebene to 1 oz olive oil, or half a teaspoon of ether to 1 oz olive oil; six grains of sulphate of iron to one gallon of drinking water will kill any larvae which may happen to be coughed into it.

Other parasitic diseases are round-worm, tape-worm and thread-worm. They are easily recognised in the droppings and are eradicated by proprietary drugs supplied by any chemist.

Lice (Mallophaga). The word Mallophaga comes from the Greek—*Mallos*—wool and *phagos*—eating.

Parasitologists have placed the humble louse on a higher sphere than something that just causes scratching. Around 26,000 species of avian lice have been recognised. Each group of birds has its own species and some species of lice belong to only one species of bird. Pheasants today carry the same lice as the wild pheasants in Asia. At the present time the species have survived the European climate over the years since they were first imported. It is in fact almost possible to classify the order to which a bird belongs by the lice it carries. The whole life of a louse, from egg to maturity, is spent on its host.

If a bird is healthy and able to dustbath and preen itself, it can keep down the louse population. If it is sick and unable to perform its toilet, the louse gets the upper hand and will reach such proportions that it will destroy its host. An old superstition is that a sickly bird will make lice—of course this is not correct, the lice simply have more opportunity to multiply. The pheasant can be infested with eight species at the same time, i.e. the body louse, head louse, wing louse, feather shaft louse, fluff louse, red mite, scaly leg mite and mange mite. Lice cause a lot of irritation and infested birds are seen to be continually scratching and preening themselves.

Red mite is a tiny grey insect which infests birds at night and feeds on blood. When filled it has a bright red colour. Dusting with commercial insecticides containing D.D.T. is effective except in the case of red mite. This is a nocturnal parasite which hides in timber cracks during the day; it can be destroyed by painting all timbers with creosote or nicotine sulphate perch paint.

Scaly leg mite infests under the leg scales. Painting the legs with paraffin will kill it.

Mange mite infests the body skin. Dusting with D.D.T. will cure it.

Fleas. A bad infestation of fleas, *Ceratophyllus gallinae*, because of their biting and sucking will keep pheasants restless especially when incubating. Occasionally dusting the nest with D.D.T. will keep them under control.

Prevention of Diseases

For the prevention of diseases in general, avoid rearing on infected ground; breed from healthy stock; observe strict cleanliness; give correct diet and cod liver oil; protect the birds from rain and keep their feet dry as much as possible. A most important thing is to remove an ailing bird immediately it is noticed; isolate it and treat it. One drop of carbolic acid to one pint of drinking water is a good bowel disinfectant. To administer cod liver oil, rub a little with the hands into the food.

Habits, Injuries and Digestive Disorders

FEATHER PLUCKING

Growing chicks will often start picking at the blood quills of each other's tails, causing them to bleed. If this is not stopped the condition may reach the stage where the tail will not grow and the bird will suffer pain. I find that a liberal dressing of paraffin to the tail covert will prevent the habit. The dressing must be repeated every few days.

Feather plucking, although not a disease, can be serious in an enclosure. If the culprit cannot be discovered, or if found cannot be done without (it may be a rare specimen), plastic spectacles can be easily fitted over the beak and they will cure the habit. The same fixture will prevent cannibalism. If one of a flock is sick or off colour, the others will pounce on it, kill it and eat it.

In a very bad case of feather plucking or cannibalism, the offender must be debeaked. This operation is very simple; get a helper to hold the bird firmly; place a small stick between the upper and lower mandibles, then put the upper mandible on the edge of a table and with a sharp knife, take off about $\frac{1}{4}$ in. Be careful not to cut the quick which can be seen by holding the beak up to strong light. A male pheasant can sometimes be very wicked in an enclosure and may murder his mate. In this case he must be removed and only returned to the enclosure for a few hours daily and watched.

EGG SUCKING

Egg sucking can be prevented by adding a little vinegar to the drinking water, or by laying artificial eggs about, or the eggs of guinea fowl, which cannot be broken by pheasants.

MOULTING

Like other birds which depend on flight for safety, pheasants do not moult their feathers indiscriminately. They follow a definite pattern. As feathers are shed there is always a reserve and as new ones mature and take on function and protection from weather, others are cast. Moulting time in aviaries with the rarer, more exotic species can be anxious. The bird's general health is at its lowest, since the moult comes on shortly after the efforts of laying and rearing and puts a great strain on the constitution.

If not in good condition a pheasant may get "stuck in the moult," which means that it is unable to keep itself preened and the new feathers are not kept cleansed of the new quill covering. The feathers do not come out in their natural beauty. They are deformed and stunted and the moult takes much longer to complete and when completed the plumage always looks damaged. Feathers are products of the epidermal cells of the skin and an unhealthy skin from an unhealthy bird cannot produce beautiful plumage.

Casualties caused by chills can be frequent if the weather is wet and cold; shelter is important and birds must be fed liberally on corn, fresh green food and cod liver oil; a little linseed will improve feather texture and sheen. Pheasants are at their best immediately after the moult, in the fall of the year, when they show off all their gorgeous reds, golds, purples and blues, against the autumn sun.

BROKEN LEGS

Broken legs are common. The best treatment is to wrap the limb with a plaster of paris bandage and keep the bird quiet in a box until it sets. Before releasing it, clip or pluck the feathers off one wing to keep it from flying. If the injured bird is a young chick, get a large quill, or one that will wrap around the leg comfortably; cut it to the length of the broken bone, slit it up the centre, apply it around the seat of the break and bind with adhesive tape. It can be removed in two or three weeks when the break will be healed. If the limb is very badly damaged it should be amputated. The stump will heal quickly and the bird will get around well by hopping on it.

BROKEN WING

To treat a broken wing, tuck it comfortably in its natural closed position against the body. Then pass strapping right around the bird, leaving the uninjured wing free; clip the latter a little to prevent the bird from attempting to fly. There should be good union in three weeks and the plaster can then be removed.

CROP BINDING

This happens from eating too much dry grain. The trouble can often end fatally. To cure it, pour a little glycerine down the bird's throat and massage the crop gently. The mass will then readily pass on. If not successful, make a small opening in the crop with a razor blade and, having evacuated the contents, sew up the opening again with catgut or a needle and cotton. It heals quickly and there are no ill effects.

EGG BINDING

If when laying eggs the bird looks suddenly ill, wings droop and food is refused, egg binding is probably the trouble. The impacted egg can be felt in the vent by the finger. Keep the bird very warm and inject warm olive oil into the vent, the egg will then be easily passed. The condition is usually caused by a sudden cold change in the weather.

INDEX